Warrior Servants

Living Ideation:

A Mental Health
Approach

*The Living Ideation book series and training modules are dedicated to those we have lost.
We all have opportunities to offer our love and energy to each other.
Connectedness is our solution.*

First Edition: March 2023

ISBN 978-1-7364889-4-2 (Paperback)
ISBN 978-1-7364889-5-9 (eBook)

www.LivingIdeation.com

This book is written for those who work in military service, fire service, law enforcement, front-line professions, and first response. It is also written for their families and loved ones. You are warriors who have dedicated your lives to helping others. You are a source of light in this world.

This book would not be possible without the Warrior Servants who have contributed their time and input to my work. All names and identifying information have been changed. Allowing me to share in all of their experiences has been an indescribable honor. This book is built with your trusting explorations and efforts.

Contents

PREFACE

I began writing Warrior Servants when I was working as an in-house clinician of a fire department and alongside the men and women of the wildland fire service. I was originally trained to recognize the symptoms and stressors of a person and then attempt to alleviate those conditions. I was there to discover what was wrong and then try to help "fix" it. The problem with this approach to mental health is it assumes that people need fixing. The problem-focused model simply doesn't work because there will always be problems, and frankly, it is a cynical way to approach things.

This is similar to the cultures and tactics of Warrior Servants. Military, Law Enforcement, Fire, EMS, Dispatch, and front-line workers are trained to solve problems and then look for ways to do it better the next time. The Incident Debrief and After-Action Review models exist because awful things happen, and we don't want them to happen the same way twice. This makes sense, but it is inherently problem-focused.

I am in no way suggesting these approaches should go away, however, I want the reader to recognize that this culture has historically tended to almost everything in a responsive nature. You come when you are called. You suit up and show up when you are needed. Mental health in your lines of work has traditionally been addressed the same way.

We take care of our own after they have fallen into the depths of addiction, depression, PTSD, etc. Most of the time, we don't know to intervene until it is too late. Think about how many divorces and addictions have occurred in your circle. Death by suicide is a significant problem in warrior cultures because the warrior rarely shows signs of pain until it is far too late. Sadly, some problems reach a point of no return.

June of 2019 threw me directly into the mix as a mental health clinician working with warriors. A local fire department lost a brother to suicide, and they knew that things needed to change immediately. The loss shook everyone who knew him to the core, and it was now obvious that the unspoken Standard Operating Procedures for pain and vulnerability needed to get flushed. The old ways of the tough, ass-kicking, warriors not needing emotional support were glaringly WRONG! The old-school practice was in line with what has been in place for generations: "I'm okay." Sorry, no one is particularly "okay" during or after a career in service.

Almost at the same time, I was tapped to help with a jarring suicide loss within the wildland fire community. Wildland fire folks, like all warrior cultures, are a special breed of people who pride themselves on doing the extraordinary. The same stigmas of warrior strength dominated them too. When I was brainstorming with fire leadership, one individual said, "What's going on?" Another added, "We've got to get ahead of this. What's a better idea?"

The answer is clear. These hard-core professionals need to begin talking about the truths of the job and how it impacts them before things hit the fan. We need to talk about health and wellness before we fall into the pains of trauma. The old saying "An ounce of prevention is worth a pound of cure" applies to the warrior cultures that have only tended to their health when it turns to injury. Mental and emotional injuries aren't very noticeable until they become obvious. Imagine shifting the incident response model of mental health into a pre-incident education model. There will always be a battle to fight or an emergency to tend to. Let's consider normalizing the emotional impacts that happen to the people in these situations, and begin prioritizing their health.

One of the basic goals of this book is to begin knowing ourselves, and each other, better. Additionally, I hope you can learn to engage in conversations about stress and the gnarly stuff before it surprises you. There will be incidents that change you throughout your career, and as you train for them emotionally, perhaps you will be a better version of the Warrior Servant.

Chapter One

WHO IS A WARRIOR SERVANT?

Life is for Service
-Anonymous inspiration to Fred Rogers

Warrior Servants are those who choose to serve in professions that require great discipline, loyalty, and drive. This doesn't mean you have to be a Frogman with SEAL Team One, a Hot Shot, or a trauma nurse to qualify. Warrior Servants are the men and women who feel the pull of helping others in a meaningful way. They bite off challenges that most shy away from. Hard work and new challenges excite the Warrior Servant. You know who you are, and you are a special breed.

Imagine how you think an ancient Spartan soldier would look and act. Hollywood movies would depict a chiseled dude with leather armor, a sensible shield, and a sword that has clear signs of kicking ass. The Spartan would likely growl as he said very few words because there was conquering to do. All business. Put on your armor, and grab your sword, it is time to get things done. This type of dominant image has permeated many of our lifestyles.

When you wake up at an ungodly hour to suit up and perform to a level of perfection, you are on the Warrior Servant's path. It is who you are. It is what you are about. Your mindset is one of duty. Time to crush it! Quite a few of our professions have actual shields (badges) that they proudly wear to symbolize these warrior traits. Mess Dress and the badges don't define the Warrior Servant.

Who are the obvious Warrior Servants? Military, Law Enforcement, Structure and Wildland Fire, Emergency Medical Service, Dispatch, Front Line Medical, Medical Examiners, etc. Who else is a Warrior Servant? Anyone who pours themselves into their work because it makes a difference to the world is a Warrior Servant. Teachers, Pharmacists, Engineers, Counselors, Physicians, Public Works, etc.

It takes so much to become who you are. It's pretty awesome! You have been arduously tested on many levels for thousands of hours and many years. You are ready and willing to prove your abilities. At face value, you are the strength of our communities, and without you, we fall. The problems arise when the Warrior Servant loses sight of who they are without the armor, shield, and duty. If you aren't in go-mode, you may not know what to do. Who are you and what are you about?

If you had difficulty answering the question about who you are outside of being a Warrior Servant, then count yourself among the many. Many of you are extremely capable and reliable in a crisis, yet you have some work to do to become more relaxed and balanced in your personal lives. One of your biggest goals is likely to have a great career and also to have a well-deserved retirement. You probably also want the loved ones surrounding you to have health, happiness, and prosperity. This would require a mindset that is flexible and tolerant. The word resilient has been thrown around so much in recent years and it has become a bit cliché, but the spirit of resiliency is pretty straightforward. The flexibility and tolerance for the grind result in enhanced strength and capability of being a warrior. These abilities also translate into the non-warrior.

Herein lies the problem with the Warrior Servant. Frequently, they don't know how to be off shift and settle down. For far too long, the Warrior Servant has over-identified with being responsible, reliable, and stoic. They should be commended for this right up to the point that those traits poisoned the things they deserve and love. There are so many divorces, empty booze bottles, adrenaline-driven accidents, and suicides because servants don't let themselves chill out and be down-to-earth humans.

Why is this? What is blocking the return to simplified living and peace? How can the loudness in your head throttle down and allow you to sleep at night? How can the shield of service be put down for a bit? Who are you underneath the armor?

These answers will come from understanding how the Warrior Servant culture became so intense. The answers lie within the stigmas and traditions that have promoted the "no pain" philosophy.

Chapter Two

MAKING SENSE OF THE WARRIOR

There comes a point where we need to stop just
pulling people out of the river. We need to go
upstream and find out why they're falling in.

-Archbishop Desmond Tutu

The Warrior Servant culture has been pretty steady
since people started writing things down. Each
generation has communicated and reinforced the
same messages into the newest ranks, and it is time to
understand ourselves a bit better. Warriors are
groomed to believe that they don't have the same
feelings as other people. Warrior Servants don't feel
the pain, fear, and grief like "normal" folks. You are
not allowed to feel those things. There is no time or
place for feeling as long as there is work to do.

Most Warrior Servant organizations and agencies
insist that their members remain strong and are
occasionally assessed for any potential "weaknesses."

This is evident in the tools and resources offered to them. The mental health assessment tools largely ask about warning signs of depression, anxiety, trauma, addiction, and self-harm. At first glance, this makes sense. Find out what is out-of-whack and put it back in place. Fix your shit.

I am willing to bet my wallet that you are quite uncomfortable being asked about your levels of emotional pain and trauma. Ratchet that up a notch and consider how awkward it is to answer questions about self-harm and suicide. The creators of the common mental health assessments were very well intended, but most of them miss the mark because they don't consider the audience. When you read the room a bit and realize that a Warrior Servant has been raised to be strong at all times, you understand the hesitation to engage in vulnerable conversations.

"Pain is weak. Train harder." This faulty thinking has reinforced the idea that talking about our experiences means we are weak. Pain is pain, and nothing more. Warrior Servant cultures have tried to harden their people against the normal experiences that everyone goes through. They have been discouraged from feeling the truths of their experiences and many have been pushed to their breaking points. They have left their professions or are crumbling into despair.

Why is this? What is the real problem? The Warrior Servant trains hard to be calm and professional during the worst moments of another's life. You are hardcore and you deliver results. You have spent your energy developing a battle rhythm, and the problems arise when you become so good at what you do that you forget who you are when you're not in battle. Perhaps you lost sight of who you are outside of the mission. Therefore, there is always a mission. Yardwork and chores are mission focused. Parenting and relationships are mission focused. Your hobbies are mission focused. You don't take your armor off and settle into the other aspects of your lifestyle.

Warrior Servants tend to believe that talking about emotions and pain is considered weak. I remember a hardened police officer telling me he thought being afraid was "spineless." I recall an instructor in a fire academy chuckling about a recruit being depressed as a "pansy who can't hack it." This backward thinking has existed for too long, and until we begin to normalize our experiences, we will continue to deny the truths of life. If the normal feelings of being human are considered to be flawed and weak, then one can never reach their full potential as a Warrior Servant.

Please stop acting like shit doesn't bother you. Of course, it does. If you insist on being so damn awesome (sarcasm) and indestructible (more sarcasm), you are insisting on a standard that cannot be held forever. The problem with the Warrior Culture is the resistance to being vulnerable and challenging dark thoughts head-on. When we are more aware and honest about how we experience our work, then we can be more open-minded to everything in our lives. This is where the magic happens.

Humpty Dumpty and the Medical Model

Up to this point, Warrior Servants have been dutiful to others while sacrificing their health, relationships, and happiness. You have paid an enormous price. Our society has not recognized those sacrifices appropriately, and there is a simple explanation. The pain, suffering, and erosion of the warrior are addressed when they have become injured or disabled. Our current approaches to care are in line with a medical model. When you are thrashed, we will put you back together again, so you are battle-ready.

Remember Humpty Dumpty? He had a great fall from a perfectly stable wall and made a big-ass mess about 30 feet below. Only then did the King's paramedics get called to try to sustain a pulse and transport him to the Emergency Department. The

King's trauma team tried to put Humpty Dumpty back together again. It didn't work very well.

The Humpty Dumpty story is the quintessential medical model. It is an illness reduction model. We wait until it is absolutely obvious and necessary to provide aid. What if we could sit up there with the big egg and talk about things for a bit? "Humpty, you do some wild stuff for a living. What's it like?" Perhaps he can offload some of the chaos and accept that it is understandable to be a little stressed out. He might notice he wasn't alone and that somebody cared about him. This would be the beginning of a mental health model.

Missing the Mark

I might lose a couple of friends over this next part. Our government and agencies have been asking Warrior Servants the wrong questions. Warriors are asked about warning signs and symptoms of decreased functioning. Fitness for duty evaluations do not assess health and fitness nearly as much as they try to determine if someone is jacked up. The employer/Supe/CO wants to know if this guy has my back or if he is a risk to me and our unit. That's not a health model that looks out for the well-being of the individual. It's not a health model at all. It is a risk management model that is looking to reduce liability and danger. Health and risk are not the same things. Suicide screening tools are an example of how the Humpty Dumpty medical model has been in play for many years.

The commonly used assessment tools for suicide screenings are not necessarily a good fit for Warrior Servant populations. Several of the most widely used applications are the Columbia Suicide Severity Rating Scale (C-SSRS), the Ask Suicide-Screening Questions (ASQ), the Suicide Risk Assessment Guide through the U.S. Department of Veteran Affairs, the SAD PERSONS scale, and an acronym created by the American Association of Suicidology, titled IS PATH WARM.

We have been trying to figure out if our warriors are a risk to themselves and others. It makes sense to know if someone is in danger, but we forgot about the other details of the person's life. We have only focused on the warning signs. Again, health and risk are not the same things. When you only ask about what is wrong, a Warrior Servant is likely to zip it up and not talk. Warriors are traditionally very hesitant to talk about pain because they don't want to appear weak. This is a cultural problem. The Warrior Servant cultures have forced this down your throats for generations. Our government and agencies have not been focused on building the warrior nearly as much as they have focused on repairing him. This is a disservice that needs to reverse course. Remember Humpty Dumpty? You can't put that dude back together very easily. Even if you do, he will have many scars.

The assessment tools and the interviews miss the mark because they jump right into the awkward shit. They go against the grain of your training to be hardcore and not reveal weakness. These tools don't respect the code and demeanor of the typical warrior. The approaches are somewhat logical: find the problems and fix the problems. You're not a machine that needs fixing, but the current approaches treat you as if you are a misfit waiting to happen. Assessment and traditional treatments diagnose symptoms and criteria of impairment. A diagnosis is a description, not an explanation.

You make a whole lot of sense when you consider everything that you have experienced. Walk in someone's boots for a while and you will likely understand what they are going through and why they do what they do. You deserve to be better understood and not labeled as ill.

Illness reduction models can trigger discomfort and avoidance, and the questionnaires target situations that are taboo and uncomfortable for Warrior Servants. They have their place and are still essential for appropriate mental health care, but the increasing rates of suicide attempts and completions have proven that we need a new approach. The current approaches ask about your intentions for dying, but they don't gauge your ability to live.

The model that waits for people to be sick before we can render care should be categorically rejected. We have ignored the obvious: embrace health within each of us and between us. Promote connectedness, curiosity, and purpose. Imagine if you were asked more about your lifestyle, health, and stability instead of being asked about being lonely, depressed, traumatized, and suicidal.

If we can begin asking Warrior Servants about ideas for living more than asking about their thoughts of death, we might understand their emotions, perceptions, and future opportunities. Gathering information about strengths and abilities might reveal opportunities to improve healthful lifestyles, affiliations, and achievements. If those conversations aren't productive, then using depression inventories and suicide assessments is always appropriate.

Chapter Three

THE SUICIDAL WARRIOR

If being hard on yourself worked, it would have

worked by now.

-Di Ana Pissarro

It is important to acknowledge that our Warrior Servant populations die by suicide at much higher rates than the general population. A simple Google search will reveal some statistics for our military service members, law enforcement, firefighters, and front-line workers. The numbers are heartbreaking. Some of our first responders and warriors are more dangerous to themselves than the line of duty. This chapter is intended to challenge you to think about suicide in new ways. Our brothers and sisters deserve more consideration, and so do you.

"Committed"

I wish I could say that our culture has evolved a bit and stopped vilifying those who die by suicide. Unfortunately, many still use the phrase "commit suicide." This is painful because "commit" rarely implies something good. "Commit" means you should be looking over your shoulder because you stole a motorcycle or swiped my wallet. John committed a crime; he committed adultery; he ended up being committed in a penitentiary.

A small change in our language will go a long way toward changing our attitudes about mental health. Stop referring to our loved ones who have died by suicide as people who committed an act. After saying "died by suicide" approximately 19 times, it becomes much more fluent and familiar. We miss those who have died by suicide as much as we miss those who have died in other ways. We might even miss them more. Instead of a phrase that sounds insulting and degrading to their memory, our loved ones deserve respect and grace.

The American Psychiatric Association publishes the diagnostic manual for mental disorders, and they are proposing eliminating the word "commit" in relation to suicide. Some folks have proposed using the word "completed" instead. I think "completed" is pretty lame too. If someone completed suicide, does that mean they have uncompleted living? My preference is to say our loved one "died" or "died by suicide."

Warrior Servant cultures have some brutal and shameful opinions about people who are depressed, traumatized, or die by suicide. This topic is complex and not easy to understand. Some people make sense of awkward situations by placing judgments on others. In a nutshell, those who are trying to understand the mindset of a lost loved one need to assign a cause. Where does one put the feelings about the reasons "why?"

My colleague, Elizabeth, and I were chatting about language and suicide. She said, "We are curious beasts, are we not? We crave explanations for the ineffable." Grief-stricken people assign a cause to death to make more sense of it. Cancer? Cancer-related death has an explanation. TMB (Too many birthdays)? Old age is the natural course of things. Car accident? Damn! How unfortunate. Drunk driver or murderer? Someone must pay. Suicide? What the hell do I do with that?

Depression, anxiety, trauma, and suicide make sense to the person experiencing them. This is like being in love and missing the person when they aren't around. It fits with the circumstances of life. It's time for our cultures to lighten up a bit with how we accept love and excitement differently than pain and despair.

The first step is to stop looking down on each other for feeling normal emotions.

I'm not suggesting that Warrior Servants need to create a hug club where we sit in a circle and offload our deepest pains, but what if we did begin to acknowledge the truth more? We hurt, we fear, we yearn, we love. Being human means that many emotions exist, and if we stop vilifying suicide, trauma, and pain, then we can have more authentic and stable lives.

Suicide Makes Sense

Death by suicide makes sense when you understand what is going on with someone. Suicide is almost always about pain and an inability to shake free from it. Let's try to understand the basic difference between people who are suicidal and those who aren't.

A person who is not considering suicide has a wide-open window of perspective. They can appreciate the good times and can tolerate the bad times. They also have an understanding that the god-awful times are temporary. The window of truth has plenty of light, and they can make decisions to manage the situation.

People who become suicidal lose the ability to see beauty and light because their window of perspective is consistently closing in. The window narrows until there is only darkness. This is a simple explanation for how depression, anxiety, and trauma can slowly crush the Warrior Servant. When one can only see the darkness of pain and they believe that things will never change, then turning the pain off is a reasonable idea.

If you truly thought your life was only pain, then it would make sense to end the suffering. Death by suicide is usually a case of unyielding, dominant pain. The darkness is permanent, and light will never return. A suicidal person has the perspective of being cursed.

I am not endorsing suicide as an option for those who are suffering. I firmly believe we are obligated to try to prevent the losses that have become too common, and we need to keep trying to offer light to those who only see darkness. First, we must stop trashing our brothers and sisters who are stuck in the shadows of pain. Suicide is rarely the stigmas and judgments that follow in the next section.

Common Stigmas About Suicide

It's selfish. Many believe that suicide is selfish because of the devastating pain the survivors feel. If the person who was taking his or her life was intending to cause harm, then this idea makes sense.

Do you think that the person was trying to hurt others or simply stop their own pain? I doubt most people who die by suicide are trying to hurt anyone else.

They are weak. Assigning weakness and a lack of mental fortitude is a common justification. The living also feel pain, yet they push through the chaos of living; those who take their own lives must surely be weak in comparison. This is invalidating and insulting to people overburdened with despair. If you understood what the suicidal person was going through, you might not think it was weak.

Suicide is cowardly. Cowardice is another negative label survivors assign to the deceased. It is too simple to believe that the person who has left our lives was a quitter rather than a resilient warrior who would not give up on life. After all the hell the person went through, it's too easy to chalk it up to a lack of courage. This is another insulting way to think about people.

Suicide is a sin. Christianity originally aligned suicide with the commandment, Thou shalt not kill. Modern Christianity saw death by suicide as the destruction of God's creation and a departure from God's will. For the faithful who lose a loved one to suicide, the grieving and reconciliation process can be complicated. The conflict is that you are longing for your loved one while simultaneously wrestling with the notion that they are in purgatory or hell. Thinking ill of the person who has died is generally inconsistent with a loving and peaceful mourning process (Alessi, et al., 2020).

They only pass on the pain. Similar to selfishness and cowardice, if a survivor can justify the absence of the suicide victim by shaming them, then that creates a message that they had poor judgment and were making a horrible decision. A person who knowingly passes on pain would be a jerk, wouldn't they? I doubt that adequately describes your loved one.

They never showed any signs. They looked so happy. This reflection is consistent with a survivor who is resistant to acknowledge that their loved one was quietly hurting inside. The negative stigma grows from the belief that the victim was putting on some sort of front or was impulsive. The conclusion is that they were irrational and not thinking clearly. If we think that the death was a rash decision, we aren't as angry with the person who is gone.

Why (fill in the blank)? There are so many "why" questions that arise after a suicide loss. The problem with "why" questions is they almost always imply wrongdoing and poor decision-making. "Why didn't they talk to me about their pain?" This question suggests that they should have said something, or they were supposed to talk about their pain. Other common "why" questions:

- Why didn't they ask for help?
- Why didn't they take control?
- Why didn't they come to me?
- Why didn't they try harder?

They were so successful. This is so out of character. Statements like this reveal the disbelief and confusion of a survivor. What you saw as success and strength also existed with much darker thoughts and situations. Most people have a difficult time understanding that people who suffer don't always show it. This is common with Warrior Servants, and the stigma implies that the person who died was hiding something. Well, frankly, they probably were concealing what they were going through.

A permanent solution to a temporary problem. This common phrase is said by people who have very different perspectives from the person who is suffering. We, outsiders, can see that life has options while people who are suicidal are frozen with inescapable darkness. The suicidal mindset truly seems permanent and thinking the person was not thinking clearly can be invalidating and critical.

Warrior culture has not been gentle with the topics of depression, anxiety, trauma, and suicide. We have not thought about the experiences of those who are suffering. Consider that a person who takes his or her life was trying to maintain dignity with their choice. Perhaps their death is an expression of honor and service. Can death by suicide provide peace? All of us deserve gentler consideration, and those who die by suicide surely do as well.

What Are Your Thoughts About Suicide?

Many of us have strong opinions about suicide, and it is important to see how our beliefs can impact those around us. Similar to talking about religion and politics at the dinner table, our beliefs about suicide can quickly spark up some drama. If I think people who take their lives by suicide are weak, cowardly, and sinful, then I might assume you think that way too. We all have opportunities to recognize our personal beliefs and put them in check. Hopefully, you can realize that the person across from you isn't a mirror image of your belief system. I challenge all of you reading this to recognize your opinions about suicide and mental health. Instead of thinking everyone else should agree with you, be curious and try to understand other's opinions.

Here is a simple exercise to get to know your thoughts about suicide:

Read and complete each statement below. Write down your thoughts if it helps clarify your beliefs.

- I think suicide is …

- People who kill themselves are ...
- Suicidal thoughts are ...

Now, those are the types of comments we typically don't say out loud to others, because saying our beliefs can be incredibly hurtful to someone else. Please think about how you feel about suicide. Imagine how you might accidentally communicate your thoughts and feelings to someone you care about. I think if you can restrain yourself, then your fellow Warrior Servants can probably trust you better. What we do, what we say, and how we interact make a huge difference to people who are struggling with pain, loneliness, despair, and suicide.

Get to know yourself and how you feel about depression, anxiety, grief, trauma, and suicide. As your self-awareness grows, you can be more neutral and compassionate. There is a boomerang effect with awareness in Warrior Servant cultures. Your cool headedness changes your relationships and most likely helps others treat you in similar ways.

If you haven't already figured out that life is unpredictable and startling at times, then you will before long. Warrior Servants jump into the pool of chaos, and they learn through action. What is overwhelming and traumatic for one is hardly bothersome to another. Let's all try to recognize that we can influence each other in compassionate ways.

Suicide Exposure and Impact on Survivors

All Warrior Servants will be touched by suicide at some point. There is, however, a huge difference in the exposure and impact they will experience. Simply, the closer the bond that one has with the victim, the higher the likelihood of being emotionally thrashed. Consider how different the responses can be:

Exposure—Impact—Grief—Depression—Debilitation

I have known several people who have died by suicide, and each loss hit me differently. I have been directly and indirectly exposed to deaths and was never affected the same way twice. I didn't know some of the people particularly well nor did their lifestyles fit with mine, so I was able to keep moving forward without skipping a beat. People whom I had a closer kinship and bond with have impacted me more deeply. I still think of them regularly because I feel like they were a part of me. The loss of a family member shattered me in a way that will never quite heal, and I will walk with an emotional limp for the rest of my days.

I share my personal experiences because I want to normalize the fact that life, and death, hurts. It hurts badly. This applies to all of us, and when you lose someone close to you, or you experience an awful incident, it is understandable that it will affect you.

Warrior Servants form amazing connections with their colleagues and families. The bonds can be difficult for people in the general public to understand. You will therefore experience the sting of loss throughout your career, and sometimes, it will level you. Based on the tight knit of your relationships, death will change how you look at the world. Perhaps it should.

Life has pain, and it also has non-pain. They must coexist. This simple philosophy is all too often left out of Warrior Servant cultures. Please know, when the pain of loss is ignored, or shoved down inside, it will mutate and boil up in ways you never considered. We all have opportunities to normalize pain while also adding new meaning to our lives.

Pressure Cookers and Tea Kettles

I was the youngest of four boys growing up, and we found ourselves in the middle of some pretty wild shenanigans. We did some sketchy shit by today's standards. Our mother would occasionally cook our meals in a pressure cooker, and we saw that as an opportunity for some entertainment. We would commandeer the device and disassemble the temperature regulator and release valve. Essentially, we would create a bomb filled with toys like plastic green army men and Matchbox cars. Without a pressure release mechanism, the locked-down vessel would violently explode. Violent is not a strong enough word for it. I will always remember the shrapnel that blew through the back wall of our shed and was embedded in the pine trees. The pot was altered and simply could not communicate until it had reached a point of destruction. Boom!

A tea kettle is heated and reaches a particular temperature only to begin sounding off. The teapot starts saying, "Hey! We're good to go. Shut it down." This allows for de-escalation, and a new experience can occur when the flame is reduced. We are sometimes like pressure cookers who don't communicate our stress until it is undeniable and dangerous, and we are sometimes like tea kettles who communicate regularly and productively.

Warrior Servants have traditionally had firm opinions about being strong and resilient. This is a pressure cooker mindset, and it will explode in time. Tick, tick, tick, BOOM! Here are a few common Warrior Servant attitudes that will hurt you at some point:

"Pain is weakness; show no weakness."
"Rub some dirt in it and keep pushing."
"Quit bellyaching and deal with it."

"Get over it and move on."

"Suck it up."

"You're not paid to think; you're paid to perform."

"The only easy day was yesterday."

"I'll sleep when I'm dead."

Perhaps you have thought, "I don't want to look weak. I need to be the Alpha dog." That's a tough way to go about life. If you think you need to always wear the false armor of strength in every part of your life, you are headed down a road that doesn't exist. Eventually, life has a way of putting us on our knees. All of us feel insecure and vulnerable to pain. We all experience sadness, loneliness, and fear. Thank goodness that we feel joy and love too. Acceptance of this human condition is our path toward greater peace and connectedness.

Most will think that normalizing our feelings is appropriate. Maybe you have come to accept that talking about your feelings can be helpful, but when it comes to suicide and dark thoughts, Warrior Servants tend to think those feelings need to be put away and kept secret. They think nobody would understand that they are curious about ending their lives. We do understand. We all understand our personal versions of pain, loss, and fear. We all fall into bouts of depression and anxiety. We all feel trauma. We all hope for shit to quiet down so that we can take a deep breath.

Talking about suicidal thoughts allows an overwhelming situation to lose steam. Just like the tea kettle and pressure cooker example, we all need to find ways to reduce the heat and pressure in our lives. Releasing pain and despair allows us to grow. If we can stop acting like we are tougher than we are, or need to be, we can begin to move through the darkness. Suicide is not a topic for people to avoid; rather, suicide is a phenomenon that deserves much more conversation.

Chapter Four

TAKE THE ARMOR OFF

*What is necessary to change a person is to
change his awareness of himself.*
-Abraham Maslow

If you and I were in an elevator together and we introduced ourselves, we most likely would describe what we do professionally: name, rank, time in service. For example, one might say, "I'm a Captain with Modesto Fire and Rescue. Only six more years until retirement." That introduction only tells me you have made your way up the ranks a bit and are counting the days until you get out. I imagine I would follow suit and briefly describe who I am as a working man.

Being a person in public service is not who you are, it is what you do. Some of you might take issue with that, but slow down for a minute and take the armor off. Underneath the job duties and work ethic is a spirit of service, honor, loyalty, and fortitude. I interviewed a Marine friend of mine and I asked him to explain the motto, "Once a Marine, always a Marine!" He told me about commitment, trust, fidelity, and a sense of purpose. He went on to tell me how he felt like he was part of a family. His military family is a group who "gets it." Those understandings are what make Marines phenomenal. It is the people who make the Marine Corps what it is. This applies to each Warrior Servant culture.

Here is an example of who my friend is: "Yes, I'm a Marine and I always will be. I'm also a badass motherfucker who will die for my friends and family. Loyal 'til I die. When I see people being treated poorly, I can't stand by and not make it right. I want everybody to be treated with respect and dignity, and if I can be a part of that, count me in."

When Warrior Servants look at themselves in the mirror, they rarely see an accurate reflection. The realities of your life and experiences are beyond the hardened stare. The person looking back at you finds it difficult to express the sadness, loneliness, fears, and doubts that crept in over the years. You don't see yourself until someone who "gets it" points out the truth. This is because you are usually the Alpha in the room who takes care of everyone else. You are the helper and not the one who asks for help.

Warrior Servants who see themselves as "on duty" all the time run the risk of impacting those around them in negative ways. "Once a Marine, always a Marine" is fantastic up to the point that your spouse and children resent being drafted into the Marines. It is time to get to know yourself a bit better and clear up your headspace.

Feel free to write on these pages (it's your book) or pull out some paper. The following question seems straightforward, but I think you will notice it becomes challenging pretty quickly. The question is: Who are you?

This is a loaded question, and most Warrior Servants will jump to an answer that describes their profession. "I'm a deputy." "I'm a medic." "I'm a nurse." "I'm a firefighter."

I imagine your chosen line of work has become the most obvious role in your life, and you have given more time to your professional duties than anything else. This common truth explains why so many Warrior Servants have experienced divorces, addictions, and early deaths. You have convinced yourself that your duty to service must come before the other roles that help make up who you are. Many of you have neglected the other roles and relationships in your life.

Before you can create a more balanced lifestyle, it is important to see yourself accurately. This exercise will help you recognize all the hats you wear. You are a person who works for a living, serves others, is in relationships, and has hobbies. List five of the primary responsibilities you have.

Here is my example:

- ❖ I am a therapist.
- ❖ I am a husband.
- ❖ I am a father.
- ❖ I am a friend.
- ❖ I am an outdoorsman.

Your turn. Write five of your primary responsibilities.

❖ _____

❖ _____

❖ _____

❖ _____

❖ _____

Now that you have listed a few of your roles and responsibilities, take a moment to put them in order of importance. Think about what they mean to you. What is truly most important to you? Is it still your career?

What is most important to me:
1. I am a husband.
2. I am a father.
3. I am a therapist.
4. I am a friend.
5. I am an outdoorsman.

Reality check. Write your list in order of importance.

1. _____

2. _____

3. _____

4. _____

5. _____

I imagine your two lists are a bit different. If they aren't, then give yourself a high-five and keep crushing life. If your lists shifted, as mine did, then there are a couple of concerns: You are putting too much of yourself into the things that don't matter as much, and you are underperforming in your starring roles.

Of course, your career of service is important and deserves great respect, but surely you recognize that you work within an organization designed to replace you four minutes after you leave. Many Warrior Servants are under the impression that their role is critical to the success of the team. To a certain degree, they are. Aren't you more essential to your family? To your spouse or partner? To your friends? To yourself?

Who are you? Without using a title, role, responsibility, or relationship, try to describe yourself in two or three words. These words should be the deep truths of your character. When you can listen to the whispers of who you truly are and what you are about, then you can move forward in your life. Until then, you will be stuck in a rigid understanding of yourself. There is a starter pack of examples on the next page. Use them or come up with your own.

Who are you?

I am _____.

I am _____.

I am _____.

I am _____.

I am _____.

Examples of words to describe you:

Kind	Honest	Trustworthy	Ambitious
Dedicated	Outgoing	Loyal	Optimistic
Generous	Empathetic	Cautious	Cheerful
Curious	Compassionate	Fearless	Creative
Passionate	Adventurous	Precise	Imaginative
Ethical	Quiet	Spontaneous	Fair
Friendly	Humble	Funny	Patient
Responsible	Realistic	Flexible	Affectionate

Willard the Frogman

Willard was a scrappy 17-year-old when he decided to enlist in the U.S. Navy. There was no Plan B. He was a notable athlete in high school, and he translated his work ethic into being one of the youngest S.E.A.L.s of his time. His career transitioned into becoming an instructor for Team One until he retired back to civilian life. Willard bit off a second career in structure fire service and found that his mindset and skills were a natural fit.

This dude doesn't have an off switch, nor does he have a dimmer switch. Willard is like many Warrior Servants who have rock-solid focus and consistency, but that's not always a good thing. If the Warrior

Servant insists those around him function at a level like his, the important relationships might crumble.

Willard strongly identifies with his professional roles, and he is also a dedicated husband and father. When asked to describe himself without listing a responsibility or relationship, he said, "I am driven. I am patient. I am unsatisfied." Driven. Patient. Unsatisfied.

Underneath the Frogman, the firefighter, the husband, the father, the friend, and the adventurer is a man whose essence is fueled by being <u>driven, patient,</u> and <u>unsatisfied</u>. These traits aren't simply tactical skills. They are going to be the keys to his future. Any time Willard feels confused, frustrated, lonely, sad, etc., he can go back to his basics. Be driven, patient, and unsatisfied.

Go to Sarah

Sarah has been a nurse in the Emergency Department of a big city hospital for 14 years. She has only worked in emergency medicine, and she says it is the only gig for her. "It's in my blood. It's what I do. It's who I am." Sarah digs the fast pace and admits that she only has two gears in life: Stop and Haul Ass.

Sarah is always willing to cover for her team and she works OT shifts regularly. Amazingly, her house and car are paid off, and she invests in her future. She is proud to be organized and responsible. This is what most of the world sees and she is praised for being this way.

She also is divorced and rarely socializes with the few friends she has met in the hospital. This woman hasn't taken a vacation in two years. When asked how she would describe herself without saying anything about her job or responsibilities, Sarah said, "I am reliable. I am compassionate. I am intense." Reliable. Compassionate. Intense.

Sarah is an amazing triage nurse, and her core traits are perfect for that culture. Sadly, she has been so good at her job that there has not been much room for close relationships and personal growth. She admits she was quite unhappy outside of nursing.

What if she could apply her qualities of being reliable, compassionate, and intense to other roles and relationships in her life? Is this realistic for Warrior Servants? Of course, it is. Imagine if a fraction of the energy Go-to Sarah gives to work was put into herself and her other roles.

Who are you?

I am _____.

I am _____.

I am _____.

Remember these truths. They are some of your core values, and they will help guide you through difficult times.

Battle Rhythm

I was talking with a group of Army vets and one of them mentioned the phrase, "Battle Rhythm." We discussed how important it was for them to have a lifestyle filled with order and routine. This was essential in the armed forces, and it applied to everyday life. I noticed that these fellows insisted on regimented goal setting and predictability. This stole some of the opportunities to relax and soak up the good things in life. It was not surprising to find most of them had been divorced and didn't have many friends outside of the Army.

The following graph illustrates the potential separation between the Warrior and the self. You can imagine that being stuck in either zone for too long has consequences. Blowing off work will create problems with your superiors, and ignoring your personal life will carry a hefty price tag. The true battle rhythm of a successful Warrior Servant fluctuates and flows consistently. What does your rhythm look like?

Battle Rhythm of the Warrior Servant

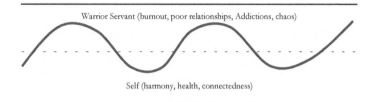

Warrior Servant (burnout, poor relationships, Addictions, chaos)

Self (harmony, health, connectedness)

The battle rhythm of so many Warrior Servants runs at a breakneck pace. It is not sustainable. The following chart might be more representative of how your life actually is. We all know people who live in get-r-done mode. That's great for a while, but for all that is gained in your career, there are probably some huge losses.

Battle Rhythm of the Warrior Servant

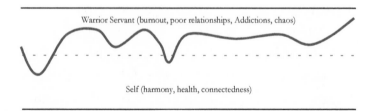

Warrior Servant (burnout, poor relationships, Addictions, chaos)

Self (harmony, health, connectedness)

Take a few things to the bank: You know someone who has experienced a terrible breakup or divorce. You know someone who has suffered from some sort of addiction. You know someone who has symptoms of trauma. You know someone who has died from suicide. These situations happen when Warrior Servants stay in the red zone of performance for too long.

The losses and sacrifices will happen if you cannot alter course. Thank you for your service, blood, sweat, and tears. You have given more than enough. Now it's time to use your skills for personal health and the future.

Chapter Five

PT vs. MT

For more than twenty years, my legs have been my second-greatest asset, propelling me over thousands of miles and on runs throughout the world. They had never failed me. But my greatest asset—which I've only occasionally lost—has been my mind.
- Scott Jurek

Most of the people who are reading this book have active careers and lifestyles. Physical Training (PT) is a regular part of your routine. Why do you PT? Write a couple of reasons below:

I PT because _____.

I PT because _____.

I PT because _____.

Maybe you PT for stress relief. It helps you stay healthy. Perhaps you have a routine that has become a habit, and you are regimented. PT might keep you from being a royal pain-in-the-ass to the people around you. The bottom line, physical training helps you stay sharp. Effort creates ability. Your body is your instrument, and you need it to be dialed.

Most will agree that keeping physically fit is non-negotiable and is expected in the Warrior Servant cultures. There are fitness assessments and task lists for most of you. You train your tails off physically and operationally. This should never stop, but you often neglect one major piece of the puzzle. You forget to prioritize your headspace as much as you value your physical abilities and skills.

Mental training (MT) has rarely been a priority. Many people don't know what the concept is. MT is quite simple; train your brain to be patient and present. Life will unfold as you make each moment. One moment at a time. There is no other way, nor can there be another way. This moment is all that exists, and the skills of MT are easy to develop and maintain. This chapter is going to put you through a few exercises aimed to help you focus your thoughts. Similar to PT, when you MT with regularity, you will achieve results. Time to get jacked!

Who Are Your People?

Earlier, you wrote down the roles and relationships that were important to you. Now I want you to write down the most valuable people in your life. These are the folks who help you be a better version of yourself. They are the ride-or-die crew who supports you through anything.

Please don't feel pressured to write the names of people who you think "should" be on the list. Who are the ones who fill you up and help you feel like your true self? Here is my example in no particular order:

My people: Baker

My people: Avery (my daughter)

My people: Jack (my son)

My people: Andrea (my bride)

My people: Holt

My people: Randy

Your turn. Who are your people?

My people: _____.

My people: _____.

My people: _____.

My people: _____.

My people: _____.

My people: _____.

Now I want you to review your list and pick the one person who knows you the best. This person knows all of your embarrassing shit and loves you more for it. This person is a part of you. Write their name below:

THE person in my life: _____.

The name you chose suddenly filled your brain with a flurry of memories and feelings. The thought of this person got your energy up in a way that it wasn't a moment ago. Essentially, your brain did a few pull-ups and burpees. Nice work! You now have a brief understanding of what MT is. Mental training is not complicated. It is you intentionally focusing your thoughts, so you are calmer and in control of your decisions.

Many Warrior Servants get caught up in the heat of a moment. This is understandable because you must perform. The problem with you being so good at your job is that you may not be capable of switching gears and destressing. If you were good at the off-duty mindset and being relaxed, then booze wouldn't be so easy to buy, and I would be out of a job. This is where MT comes in, and you can do most of this on your own.

The person you labeled as the single-most-important one in your life deserves a little attention. Bear with me and trust this exercise. I am quite confident that it will help and not hurt your relationship. I want you to take out your phone and write them a text. Describe what they mean to you in a couple of sentences. Use my example as a jumpstart if you can't find any words:

Text to Andrea: "I don't tell you how much you mean to me often enough. I love you so much! I can't wait to get home and spend some time together."

When you take a moment to send someone your warm thoughts, you don't lose any points in the game of life. You intentionally offered them your appreciation, hopes, and love. That is MT in a nutshell. You can focus on someone important in your life and then commit those thoughts to action. Warrior Servants are action-oriented. Loosen the knot of rigid thinking and apply it to the relationships that matter.

Take the example of the text to my wife, when I think about her and then put it into action, I am essentially calling my shot. Wanting to spend time with her usually leads to spending time with her. It might be a few weeks before we can make it happen, but it will damn well happen!

Here is the best part of MT: what you think about and then act on usually comes back to you. She texted me back and returned the kind words. My day was better because I had something nice to say, and it helped her day be a bit brighter too. Her words helped pick me up, and I had a little bit more energy for the grind.

MT fitness is achieved by putting a little bit of yourself out there with the hopes that it will positively impact someone's day. A Warrior Servant does this every day, and it works on two levels. Your efforts probably improved somebody's day, and it helped change your attitude too. Putting yourself out there is a potential double-win. Helping others comes naturally to the Warrior Servant; however, applying the same concepts of service to yourself can prove to be difficult.

The skills of discipline, training, fitness, and routine are the essence of public service. Your careers are built on being steady. These habits and abilities are all it takes to be a rock-steady individual outside of the Warrior Servant culture. You simply need to know which direction to go.

North and South

Imagine you were tasked with completing a compass course in a dense wilderness. Your mission is to reach a location due north and 10 miles away. There are mountains, rivers, and countless obstacles in your way. Many of you might think that knowing your northern heading will be your most important task, and in the wild, that adds up.

When it comes to MT and keeping your cool, I believe it is far more important to recognize the southern direction. Your inverse compass heading is what you want to pay attention to so you can stop going in the wrong direction and eventually find your way to your goal. "I want a happy life. I want a successful life." Good to know. That's north. North is the best version of who you are. Unfortunately, life gets a little blurry on the road to happiness, and we lose our way. We make mistakes and don't always make the best choices. That's south.

If you can recognize when you are on the road heading south and your life is getting a bit out-of-hand, then you can engage your brain for a slowdown. Recognizing the need for a reality check is the key to your success. You can begin the turn from southward to something more productive. Sounds easy, right? The key is your awareness and timing.

How do you know when it's time to get the alignment straightened out on your vehicle? Your car won't hold its lane and it keeps drifting. You notice your vehicle is not going where you want it to go. How did this happen? Damnit, too many curbs! Your southern heading is important to recognize because it allows you to be more aware and create change. Real life is quite a bit more complicated than wheel rash. Recognizing your southern compass headings in your habits, your work, your marriage, your parenting, etc., can be a tall task. This book is a space to work this out and become a better version of yourself.

You're Going The Wrong Way! (How does he know where we're going?)

Wildland firefighters usually work a nutty schedule of 14 days on with two days off, assuming they aren't extended longer. Typically, when these folks stop grinding, they crash hard. On the initial day off, many throw their clothes in the wash, buy a 30-rack of beer, eat an impressive amount of food, and then pass out. When they rise the next day, they will hopefully remember to put the clothes in the dryer, eat more food, and nurse a hangover. Then they will go to the store to stock up on Ibuprofen and nicotine before heading back to their crew. The pendulum of life swings between working exceptionally hard and partying like it is your last day on earth. This is not a long-term strategy for life. Warrior Servants rarely slow down and consider how these patterns impact themselves and those around them. This is where MT and being a little bit more focused on the present moment helps.

MT is a very personal concept. In a sense, you are playing a one-player game in life, and each of your decisions unfolds into a future of limitless possibilities. Only you know which direction you are going in. Below is a list of common stress/trauma reactions (van Dernoot Lipsky & Burk, 2007). They are examples of South.

- Feeling helpless/hopeless
- A sense that I can't ever do enough
- Hypervigilance
- Diminished creativity
- Inability to embrace complexity
- Minimizing
- Chronic exhaustion/Physical ailments
- Inability to listen/Deliberate avoidance
- Dissociative moments
- Sense of persecution
- Guilt
- Fear
- Anger and Cynicism

- Inability to empathize/Numbing
- Addictions
- Grandiosity/Inflated sense of importance

Exceptional scholars put together what is the most uncomfortable palm reading ever. The 16 signs of trauma exposure and response offer a glimpse into what you have likely been going through, and if you stay in your career for long, you will develop moral injuries. Warrior Servants perform duties that test their patience, tolerance, and sense of justice. This list should hit pretty hard and remind you that you aren't fooling anyone. Trauma and stress leak out in ugly ways.

This book is about being honest with yourself, so I will contribute some of my vulnerable truths. When I am short-tempered, nothing good is coming from my actions. When I notice I am becoming cynical, that's not north. When my head is down and I am grinding through work, I have forgotten to notice the beauty around me. I'm not appreciating the environments around me, and I have lost sight of my freedoms. I think I am stuck. I recognize that I start judging people more when I am tired, and I am much more thin-skinned. My ego is super fragile when I am southbound.

The following "headed south" trait is harder for many of us to talk about: alcohol and drug use. It is a common coping strategy for many Warrior types, and I am not immune to it. While whiskey and I broke up several years ago, I notice I drink more beer when I am swamped with responsibilities.

I'm not saying there isn't room to get a little bit rowdy from time to time, but when you lose sight of how much you are drinking, there might be a problem arising. The first drink goes down super-fast, as if gravity took over and splashed it into your stomach. The second drink......Holy hell! That tasted amazing! Now you feel a bit more relaxed, and the day is somewhat tolerable. The third drink? What are you up to?

MT and being aware of your present moment are keys to transitioning south into the north. When you drink the first drop of the third drink, you are probably drinking for a reason. What's the difference between having one drink and six? Five. But seriously, the difference usually has something to do with why you are drinking.

What's the reason? Maybe you are celebrating or honoring someone. Whatever your reason, that's your deal, but more often than not, you're using alcohol and drugs as volume control. You are dialing down the loudness of your day. That has been southbound trouble for me in addition to being short-tempered, cynical, inattentive, and judgmental. How about you? Do you recognize you sometimes get in your own way? Can you settle in and give yourself some honest feedback?

Here is where the rubber meets the road. To be more powerful in your life, you must be able to recognize when you are losing ground. A Marine friend of mine told me about a simple concept: "Son, you better learn how to unfuck yourself!" That can only be accomplished by recognizing what your South is. I want you to write a few southern compass headings down. Use the list from a couple of pages ago or come up with your own.

I am headed south when

_____.

I am headed south when

_____.

I am headed south when

_____.

Intermission: Now that you have dug a little deeper than you might have wanted to, please put this book down and change your headspace. You might find comfort by washing your hands and splashing cold water on your face. Taking a stroll around the house or yard can feel good too. Maybe a snack or refreshment would be appropriate. When you MT, you have earned some healthful rewards. Please take care of yourself.

The War Feels Normal

You can apply the concepts of MT to an important unspoken truth in your profession. Warriors don't know how to relax very well. They know how to soldier on. Redeployments, OT shifts, and being voluntold are normal paces of play for the over-identified servant. Ask yourself a few questions:

- If I took some time off, how long would it take me to start feeling relaxed?
- Could I turn my phone off? Off! As in powered down.
- Am I as connected with my close family-like people as I am with my crew/unit/team/ shift mates?
- When not working, are I bored and uninspired?

If any of these questions are a bit uncomfortable then you likely are over-identified with being a Warrior Servant.

You likely have been immersed in your work and neglected your personal life. This is consistent with those southern headings that you previously worked on. Remember, recognizing when you are heading south is more important than knowing when you are on the right track. The battle rhythm has been running too hot for too long, and you are losing touch with what is truly important.

Own the fact that you don't know how to dial in and take the armor off. Then you can ask, "how did this happen?" Please know this is common and can get better.

Stress, Stress, and More Stress

Warrior Servants are comfortable in high-stress situations. Stress comes with the job, and it tends to run through your veins. Each moment comes with high stakes and there is little room for error. The 11th Commandment would be: Thou shalt not fail.

Many of you train arduously for peak performances while under pressure, and you usually accomplish your goals. Focusing on the emergency in front of you is usually achievable and the stress of each moment is tolerable. You can handle it. Unfortunately, each stressful situation builds upon the others. You are asked to "handle it" over and over and over. At some point, the accumulation is too much to bear. Holding a one-pound weight in your pack is nothing, but holding 127 one-pound weights is damn near impossible.

There is a difference between situational stress and stress that has accumulated. Situational stress comes from a single event, but the darkness and pain of a career's worth of stress changes a person. It might take a long time, and a ton of bad events to be noticeable, but you'll know it when it happens. Stress matures and it mutates. It becomes heavy. It dominates every part of your lifestyle.

Accumulated stress is the whole enchilada, and it dominates every part of your life. Your professional and personal attitudes are damaged because of the buildup of trauma and stress. The last season, last deployment, last set, and last shift are stacked on top of all the others. The house of cards is many stories high. Here's the toughest part, the stress that you have endured over the years is probably impacting how you think about your future.

Many Warrior Servants project their stress into the unwritten future, and they tend to have "what if" and "what's going to happen next" questions rolling through their heads. Say, hello to the buildup of stress and understand that it is likely to stick around in most aspects of your life. If you expect that today is going to be stressful, it is going to be. You are looking for stress because it has become the norm.

If you thought that your CO was a micro-manager who always nagged at you, then I guarantee that you will be looking and listening for proof. You got in the habit of expecting familiar stressors, so you wait for the evidence to appear. What if your Captain greeted you with a cheerful, "good morning" and a box of Crispy Cream doughnuts? That's pretty cool. Then he tells you the training and chore list for the day. What a dick! The accumulated stress creates a self-fulfilling prophecy where you keep noticing the negatives more than the positives. This can be a hard habit to break.

Traditionally, Warrior Servant cultures only train for situational stress responses. When a critical incident happens, you mobilize and address the incident. Fire needs suppression; injury needs care; famine needs food; danger needs safety. There are Standard Operating Procedures for every situational stressor that we can think of, but when there is an accumulation of yesterday, today, and tomorrow, you will need to think about your stress a little bit differently.

Stress snowballs quietly throughout your career. You can grind through a small window of time and then take the edge off a bit. Unfortunately, taking the edge off doesn't address the growing pile of stress and trauma. It becomes apparent when something finally gives out. The stress cannot be ignored any longer. That looks like a broken marriage, a loved one who doesn't care to stay in contact, a demotion, a DUI, health problems, etc.

If you are always living as if you were on duty, then you are not huggable to your spouse, not a thoughtful parent, and your friends don't want to hang out with you. If we can get ahead of the maturation of stress, perhaps we can reduce it a bit. What if we could reduce it almost entirely?

MT won't fix any of your problems. MT will smack you upside the head and help you see the truth of your stress. You can fix your problems as you become more self-aware. It will help you realize that life does not need to be as complicated as it has been, and you can begin to alter course. Better days are ahead.

Check Your Compass

Take a breath. Take a second breath. The idea of MT is like PT. You must become aware of your situation and train toward your goals. As you begin to understand your stress and trauma, you are in a position to train up. The following exercise is to help you know yourself a bit better. When you have a better understanding of a situation, you can begin to steer North.

What are a few words to describe your mindset when you are in Warrior Servant mode?

_____

_____

_____

_____

_____

Common examples of the Warrior Servant headspace are:

- Committed (sometimes over-committed)
- Engaged
- Excited
- Focused
- Groundhog Day (overly repetitive / monotony)
- Disciplined
- Two more chains (Are we there yet?)
- Improvise, Adapt, Overcome
- Dutiful
- Proud

- Plan and react
- Semper Gumby (always flexible)

The examples for your Warrior Servant headspace are truths that have come from many hours, days, and years of training. Your training is now in your blood, and it almost becomes who you are in every aspect of being. You are the go-time, let's hustle, get it done, crush it type of person. You were a self before you became the warrior, and now the warrior is part of the self. You can't surgically remove the warrior from the self, nor should you, because there is a rock star, badass nature to the Warrior Servant.

Whatever your answers were, I want you to own up to them. Your answers aren't wrong or right; they are the truth of your experience. If you remember the North vs. South concept from a few pages ago, you will find that some of your mindsets and attitudes have turned southward. That's important to recognize. Recognizing when you are on a path leading away from happiness and fulfillment is your key to change.

Now shift your thoughts and offer a few words to describe your life outside of being a professional. Who are you when you are simply a person who exists in the world, outside of service? What is life like for you when you aren't wearing a uniform or performing your duties? Imagine being in any/all roles outside of your work. You exist in relationships and environments other than service. What comes to mind when you think of your best buddies, your lover, or your kids? How do you feel when you imagine being on vacation for 10 days? Again, there are no right or wrong answers. There are your answers, and your honesty will set you up for growth.

What are a few words to describe your mindset when you are in non-Warrior Servant mode?

_____

_____

_____

_____

_____

_____

_____

Common examples of the non-Warrior Servant headspace are:

- Relaxed / Slowed down
- Refocused
- Disengaged
- Decompressed
- Family time
- Happy

- Bored/Stressed (The Warrior is peeking through!)
- Rejuvenated – Ready for the next assignment
- Ops normal

These are telling answers. Both lists have a flurry of different feelings and stress levels, and I bet your heart rate fluctuated quite a bit as you read the common responses. This makes sense and is a good sign that you are in a position to create some changes in your life.

Typically, Warrior Servants don't know how to blend their work brains with their non-work brains. When you are on task, you are focused and tightly wound. You need to be. However, when you have moments to reconnect with the things that make you happy, you don't know how to downshift. The switch for work mode doesn't shut off very well.

What comes to mind when you think about your non-Warrior Servant mode? Who are the people in your life when you aren't battling and grinding? What would you be doing if you weren't being so awesome for others? What are you proud of besides your career?

Imagine going to family events. How long has it been since you were in a photograph with them? What if you dusted off your cooking and barbecue skills? Can you recall some of your favorite recipes?

If you pulled out your old golf clubs, you might realize that they feel pretty good in your hands. Then you would most likely go hack at a few dandelions on the lawn.

There is probably a huge discrepancy between on and off. That is the reason I asked you to describe your separate headspaces. Those differences lend a better understanding of stress, trauma, anxiousness, and depression. It also helps explain how so many Warrior Servants have broken relationships and divorces. But wait, there's more. Your inability to relax your head also justifies so many alcohol and drug problems. Sadly, it also can lead to suicidal mindsets.

I'm asking you to see yourself clearly. There are no right or wrong answers in the game of life, and there is no grade in the class. What you have gone through is valid. When you can see more clearly, you can tend to yourself more accurately.

Be a Beginner

This might be a little uncomfortable for you. I'm asking you to consider being a beginner. "C'mon, man! We don't have time to be a beginner. We've got to get out there and get after it. There's little room for error, and there's no room for failure." You are a high performer and you have been part of an A-Team for quite some time, so having a beginner's mindset might be strange for you.

A Warrior Servant is a professional badass who can take pride in knowing that they are the right person for almost any occasion. Being an expert in life must be a heavy burden. This closed mindset can be dangerous when there is no room for growth and new ideas. Experts have nothing new to learn because they know it all. What if all of us dialed back the need to be an expert?

Being a beginner means that you have an open mind and that you aren't everything to everyone. Trust your compass and recognize when you are headed south. Beginners can learn from the southern winds and then allow for new opportunities. North happens, and it will always be there. The beginner's mindset is essential to MT. Be an excited rookie with your outlook and be eager for new opportunities.

Chapter Six

LIVING IDEATION

New beginnings are often disguised as painful endings
- Lao Tzu

Many of you have been trained to pay attention to chaos and be ready to address whatever comes your way. You have become prepared to watch for any sign of trouble. That might include the medical signs of distress and harm, a cold front blowing in for a red flag day, a suspicious vehicle loitering in the neighborhood, and an enemy adjusting their position. This is similar to how mental health models have been developed. "Watch out for the warning signs and behaviors." Look out for your brother and sister, and wait for them to need your help.

Looking for danger is normal for Warrior Servants. Those of us who work with people in emotional crisis are trained to look for suicidal ideations. Ideations are simply thoughts and behaviors, but the term is typically used with suicide, depression, anxiety, and trauma. The focus is on illness and problems, and it's pretty dark most of the time. It makes sense to look for the signs and symptoms of danger, but we have neglected to think about how ideations (thoughts and behaviors) can be applied to living. What if we regularly asked about the thoughts and behaviors of living instead of dying? Living Ideation is a model that I developed over the years, and it has grown from a counseling approach into easy-to-use techniques for almost anyone. Like what Red said in Shawshank, "Get busy livin', or get busy dyin'."

Living Ideation focuses on the present and future. Give yourself credit for knowing how to live, develop, and prosper. You are damn good at living. After all, you've made it this far! Life is a series of choices, and each choice leads to another choice. Maybe our choices don't need to be restricted to this moment that seems unfulfilling. Living Ideation encourages us to settle down and focus on what could happen if we were calm, curious, and a bit brave. That's what Warrior Servants are good at.

Before we can help others, we must learn how to improve ourselves. Living Ideation helps warriors stop the stuck mindsets that have developed over the years, and it encourages them to build upon their existing strengths. The North/South concept from earlier is key to improving your skillsets, and in time, you can be thankful for the horrible things that you have gone through. Your pain, fear, and loss can all be converted into realizations of strength and perseverance. You have weathered amazing storms, and you are still here to talk about it. It's time to focus on how capable and strong you are rather than focus on what you think are weaknesses and inabilities.

Talking about pain and darkness is hard, and most people don't want to touch that stove on purpose. It's hot, and it will always be hot. Normalizing the difficulties of life is not the only option. Living Ideation helps people understand their dilemmas, ponder meaning, and create newness. We can begin to expand what is beautiful and good in our lives. If we can find a way to understand ourselves a bit better, then pain serves as an opportunity to change directions and create a rewarding future.

Living Ideation is about building up what already exists rather than repairing what became damaged. It is a process of developing your awareness of the traumas and dramas in life so you can flip those lessons into strength and ability. Living Ideation explores what can be meaningful in your life. That's an open-ended opportunity for the rest of your life.

Directionality and movement of life

Many think that depression and suicide are situations where someone is wasting away, and they are moving toward death. Slow down and consider that these mindsets are usually moving away from life. There is varying directionality between living and dying. The directions are toward the self, away from the self, and an exchange of both.

Suicide, depression, anxiety, and trauma can convince a person that life is moving backward and it's as if you were a salmon moving upstream. Arduous. A suicidal person's movement is atrophied and destructive. The death direction is funneling into absence. The inward-focused pain is dominant, and there is hardly any relief. Darkness slowly closes in. Can you start to understand the direction of pain?

Take a few moments to acknowledge the directionality within your own life. Are the vitality and air that you crave building or depleting? Are you suffering inwardly like many Warrior Servants who bottle up their emotions? Do you express your feelings and experiences to others? That's outward. If you are engaging in a conversation, then the directionality and movement of your energies are exchanged. Perhaps you could say that the direction is outward and productive.

Deputy Paul

Paul, a young deputy, was dedicated to being successful in his career. He was first in his class, and he excelled at everything that was put in front of him. This dude was a model cop. He thought he had it all: a dream job, brotherhood, money in the bank, health, and a promising relationship. Three weeks after the academy, his longtime girlfriend dumped him and moved out.

Suddenly, Paul had the reality check that he had given all his time and energy to his department. He outwardly gave his sweat and time while inwardly he told himself to "shut up and grind." His commitment to the job ignored the girl of his dreams. This slowly eroded their relationship and she had to leave. Paul was confident that she would come back and realize he was ready to commit to her. Every time he tried to talk to her and make up for the past, she shut him down. Paul crumbled and thought that he was a failure. His sleepless nights spun his thoughts into loneliness and isolation. He was imploding and the self-criticisms were a constant attack on who he used to be.

When Paul discovered that the love of his life had begun dating a cop from another department, his embarrassment and grief hit a new low. Paul couldn't shake it and he stopped going to work. When the department barked that he needed to report back immediately, he threw his phone away. His grief and sense of failure were inescapable. The inward chaos had become too much for Paul, and he made a plan to kill himself.

Paul washed a handful of sleeping pills down with a glass of Maker's Mark and climbed into a hammock to die. Paul was drifting quickly into oblivion, and he yearned for the quiet that he imagined death would bring. Paul had become lost within himself, and the downward spiral was at its end. Paul wasn't trying to die, nor was he trying to live. He was attempting to end pain.

Paul's eyes fluttered open as a strange sensation stole his attention. A bird flew over him and defecated on his forehead. As he wiped his head and looked at his hand, he muttered, "what the fuck?" His disbelief turned into a moment of laughter. How on earth was he ready to quiet the chaos and then be covered in bird shit? It was comical. He rolled out of the hammock, dug his phone out of the trash, and called his training officer. "I need help. I need it now."

Paul sat on my couch many times in the aftermath of his suicide attempt, and he told me how his inner dialogue had been dominated by negativity. He stopped connecting with others and his sense of gratitude was gone. The bird incident shook his perspective, and he was curious about the weird-ass possibilities in life. Paul began to realize that the outward possibilities of family, friendship, spirituality, and service could outweigh his self-doubts. He learned how to notice the small, normally unnoticed, details of living. The directionality and movement of life took over. He surged into the next chapter of his life and re-engaged with the Sheriff's department and his loved ones. Paul is doing great things in this world now, and he has a strong sense of what darkness and light can bring.

Living Ideation recognizes that inward-facing demons are difficult to describe, and Warrior Servants are quick to hide them away. You can feel such tremendousness, yet you lock it down. In the case of Paul, he was locked up feeling profound levels of shame and grief. It almost killed him. Give him credit for being able to feel with such strength. What an ability! In time, Paul was able to use that ability as a new skill set. He turned his inward-focused pain into outward opportunities. He expressed and experienced whatever came to mind, and his thoughts and actions had meaning. He was free.

Skin-deep and soul-deep change

If you've ever thought that people don't change, then zoom out a bit and think how you were three years ago, ten years ago, twenty years ago. Of course, people change. You have, and you are destined to continue changing.

The business world uses the terms transactional and transformational changes, and they describe levels of productivity. For example, when you are asked to turn in a report, you checked the box and kept your supervisor off your back. That's a transaction. When you write up the report and try to level up in your profession, then that is a transformation. Can you see the differences between growth and development versus keeping things stable?

I use the terms skin-deep and soul-deep changes when I refer to how people live. This is more about meaningful growth and development as a person who is important in this world. When a person makes slight changes to their behavior or environment, that is a skin-deep change (transaction). Essentially, they shifted their behavior a bit but didn't alter their mindset. When people change their perspective and how they approach life, they are making soul-deep changes (transformation).

If we consider the phenomenon of clinical depression, taking an SSRI medication is a skin-deep approach to alleviating depression. You are anti-depressed. You didn't become happier with the pills. Happiness and fulfillment are up to you. Soul-deep changes might come from a change in lifestyle and perspective. When you start becoming a better version of yourself, then you are having soul-deep realizations.

A good therapist can do more than help you do things differently; good therapy helps clients become healthier versions of themselves. The classic comedian, Bob Newhart had a funny bit where he was a skin-deep therapist. When the distressed client would talk about his worries, Newhart would dramatically pause before saying, "Well, stop it." This doesn't help much. For instance, if you stop drinking alcohol, then you probably reduced the chances you will do things that you regret, but it didn't necessarily change how you cope with your stress. The skin-deep change is sobriety. The soul-deep changes are new outlooks on life and the creation of healthy habits.

A common example of skin-deep and soul-deep with traditional suicide prevention might go like this: If the person is deemed to have a suicidal mindset, let's remove all the guns from their house. Do you think that changes his mindset? That would be a skin-deep change. Please don't misinterpret my words to think I don't support removing lethal means from a suicidal person. What we are looking for is a combination of the skin-deep behavioral changes added to the soul-deep growth that comes with being a healthier person. Soul-deep work encourages you to think about how large life could be. What does it mean to die? What might it mean to live?

Take it in, look under rocks, taste your food

I traveled to D.C. for a conference in mid-2019, and I felt the urge to do something memorable. I was compelled to create a meaningful experience that could be retold for many years. I decided to wake up at 5 am, my body was still on west coast time, and take a run around the Mall. I barely noticed the humidity as I ran a couple of miles to the Lincoln Memorial. I had a quick expression of gratitude and then I sat on the steps and watched the sunrise. In my mind, I was the only human there. I was calm. Happy. Proud.

The point I want to underscore is that the components of Living Ideation already exist. While I was sitting at the feet of Lincoln, my life was chaotic, and I was very stressed. All the while, I was still able to feel calm, happy, and proud. Chaos and peace coexisted. I would have imploded if I was only able to feel the chaos. I was able to add a sense of peace and ability to the moment. I was ready to grow.

I want you to prove it to yourself.

- Find a seat for a couple of moments and think about the relationships and the roles that you have. You are an individual who is part of many groups of other people.

- And now I want you to get a little bit personal. I want you to imagine people you love. Maybe you are a son or daughter. A sibling. A parent. A friend. A spouse. A lover.
- I want you to think of somebody specific, and maybe hear them laugh. See them smile.
- Pick one person in your life, one special person in your life, and I want you to think about what you would tell them right now.
- Notice how warm and simple those thoughts are.

Now, I want you to apply that warmth and simplicity to other roles in your life. Whatever the role is, imagine how much energy and thought you put into the people around you. Remember the laughter of that special person? Think about your family, your employer, your teammates, and your friends. I want you to consider how they're doing right now.

Here is a simple truth; they're doing better because you're in their world. When you put some thought and effort into your relationships, they continue to blossom. We all can grow. We can steer many of our thoughts and situations with the positivity that we already have in abundance. Every moment gets to be new.

Warrior Servants have a knack for paying attention to important details. Getting it right is paramount. Unfortunately, many of you have become stuck in the lane of being "mission-focused." That mission will never be complete and it's stressful. Perhaps you have lost perspective and forgotten that life is pretty simple. Here are two examples of the innocence and flavor of our opportunities.

Several years ago, I was cutting down a Christmas tree on Crystal Peak in the eastern Sierras. As I was hacking away, I stopped to look for my 7-year-old son. I noticed him across a ravine where he was on the downside slope of a large rock. He was trying to turn it over. Frightened, I hollered, "Jackie, stop! What are you doing?" I could imagine him getting rolled up by the boulder.

He stopped and confidently yelled, "I'm just wondering if anyone has ever looked under this rock!" He was being an explorer and owning the moment. His innocence calmed me, so I put down the saw and we rolled the rock over together. I thought that I was being the dutiful father by cutting down a tree. Then I was the nervous and angry dad. Ultimately, I shifted into a loving parent who could share an adventure with his boy. Our eyes feasted on the most common dirt that no one has ever seen. Curiosity is a concept full of life. It is a constant renewal, and we can take advantage of it at any time.

I still think about Anthony Bourdain often. I admired everything about his show: he traveled all over, tried really cool stuff, and he was kind of a jerk who didn't care what folks thought of him. There was a part of me that wanted to be like him. A quote of his still gives me pause. Bourdain said, "Maybe that's enlightenment enough to know that there's no final resting place of the mind. No moment of smug clarity. Perhaps wisdom, at least for me means realizing how small I am, and unwise, and how far I've yet to go." Bourdain's comment isn't a dark mindset, rather, I think it is what Zen Buddhism refers to as a beginner's mindset. So, imagine how Anthony Bourdain's thoughts could apply to yourself. If we have a beginner's mindset, and we can relax in this moment, then our potential health is much greater than depression and pain. Awareness and curiosity are the keys to this. Bourdain would adventure through moments, and you could see the wonderment of every dish he consumed. Anthony Bourdain influenced a simple concept that I try to live by: Taste your food.

Connectedness

I would like to invite you into a moment of vulnerability. Recall what you were doing on the most recent 15th of March. Picture your life and all of those who were important to you. Imagine someone who you love very much suddenly died that day. Maybe it is one of your children. A partner. A sibling. One of your parents. A friend who is like a family member. A dear colleague. Sit with the thought for a couple of moments.

Now that you have a person in mind, contemplate the impact on you. As of March 15th, they are gone. Imagine the impact. Feel the size of the hole left within you. Estimate everything that the person left behind. Who doesn't get to meet this loved one? The overall loss is indescribable. Can you feel the presence and absence?

Consider taking 90 seconds out of your routine right now and writing a quick note or text to that loved one. After all, they are still alive to receive your message. Perhaps your words will change the course of their day. Could the gesture alter the direction of your day too?

I usually take those small windows to write a love note to my wife or I try to bring a smile to the faces of my kids. I even dust off the prankster within me and send crass jokes to my mother in Arizona. I find that when I take a few seconds out of my life to be in a relationship, the results are amazing. This is a simple ripple effect, and it is incredibly powerful.

The connectedness we have with others is extraordinary. We, human folk, kind of have a superpower to be intertwined with others in profound ways. We love, we hate, we anticipate, we create, and we mourn. We're all the same, and we all put our socks on one at a time. Living Ideation relies on our ability to be connected to anyone at any time. When we can lean on each other, isolation and loneliness tend to evaporate.

Charlie Brown Theory

My research has examined the depths of darkness, and as hard as I try, I have never found the edge of it. Back in 2010, I was deeply immersed in one of my projects and the work was taking over my thoughts. I needed to reset my head, so I left my keyboard and poured a cup of coffee. I decided to sit down and read the comics from the Sunday paper. That's when things got weird. I was reading the Peanuts comic by Charles Schultz when I became concerned with Charlie Brown's mental health. In my head, Charlie Brown had several warning signs of being suicidal (Murray, 2008; Shneidman, 1993).

The dark pool of research that I was swimming in had shifted the whimsical stories of an elementary school kid into a clinical assessment. The most important psychological needs include having a sense of belonging (affiliation), being able to experience pleasant emotions (non-pain), and having pride in the things that they do (achievement).

Schultz was a master at guiding young Charlie Brown through the difficulties of being a misfit amongst his peers. Many of the stories depicted Charlie Brown being heckled and all alone. His dog, Snoopy, would frequently run away and cold-shoulder his master. Charlie Brown always wanted to be a part of the gang (affiliation), yet he was regularly shunned for his foibles. He continually suited up to play baseball or participate in the spelling bee (achievement) only to get blasted by his competitors. Dear ol' Chuck tried to find happiness by having a crush on the red-headed girl in his neighborhood only to be ignored (inability to avoid pain). Remember the Christmas tree incident? The poor kid paid a price for that decision.

If Charles Schultz didn't habitually bend the adventures back to a level of comfort and compassion, the reader might have wondered about Charlie Brown's mental health. Many of the comics show him all alone. While he was on the baseball team, he was always the pitcher. Amazingly, all the batters had the knack of hitting a line drive at Charlie Brown where his clothes are literally blown off. He had physical pain on top of consistent emotional pain. He lacked affiliation and was mocked consistently. He was embarrassed and banished by his peers often.

Never once did he kick the football that Lucy Van Pelt teed up for him.

Charlie Brown never stopped trying. Again, if the author didn't gracefully create meaning with the adventures of the Peanuts troop, and if you consider the three variables of affiliation, ability to avoid pain, and achievement, Charlie Brown might have been in a really dark place.

Many of us can relate to Charlie Brown's words when he says, "What's wrong with me?" "Argh!" and "Good grief!" That's a tough way to go about things, right? So now, consider your own life and the lives of the people who we cross paths with. Think about the people who are calling upon us to serve as helping professionals. We encounter people like Charlie Brown often. We have opportunities to be more like Charles Schulz and counter the struggles with affirmations of connectedness, accomplishments, and joy.

Helplessness and Tremendousness

A couple of winters ago, I was asked to assist in a Critical Incident Stress Debriefing (CISD) for a ski patrol. Debriefings usually include the warriors who have gone through a situation that tested their limits, abilities, and duties. Usually, folks who join first responder professions are eager to serve, and my role was to have their backs and serve them.

The scenario went as follows. The final sweep of the hill is performed by the patrollers at the end of every day. They go up the lifts and visually examine the terrain to make sure that all snow-goers are down the hill. One rookie patroller saw what he thought was a skier in a tree well a few yards off-trail in the powder. When he got to the top, he sped toward a scene that confirmed his worst fear. He encountered a man who had collided with a tree before sinking into the deep well. The young patroller called for assistance on his radio and then proceeded to perform CPR. As the rescue team arrived and gave their best efforts, the skier died from a combination of head trauma and suffocation from the snow.

The debrief collected the experiences of each participant and then proceeded to weave the team back toward productivity and resiliency. During the conversation, the rookie ski patroller confided that he had a heavy sense of helplessness throughout the event. He recalled that he tried to do everything right like he had been trained, and he couldn't get the man's heart rate to stabilize. He was helpless. Helpless. The patient died.

Several minutes later, a veteran patroller chimed in and offered some feedback. The elder observed the rookie during the event and found the effort to be tremendous. The rookie was credited with doing everything in his power to resuscitate the lifeless man. I recognized that the young man relaxed a bit with the confirmation he had truly done all that he could.

How can perspectives of helplessness and tremendousness exist at the same time? The spectrum of an experience offers us opportunities to consider autonomy and freedom to choose a moment. Look at the spectrum below:

HELPLESSNESS ◄━ ━ ━ ━ ━ ━► **TREMENDOUSNESS**

The debriefing of a tragic event revealed the simultaneous perspectives of deep darkness and inspirational light. Wow! Perhaps the truth of the moment resided in the middle of both helplessness and tremendousness. The power to choose a mindset rather than be saddled with pain is within everyone. The opportunity to fluctuate between mindsets is the crux of Living Ideation. In one moment, we perceive helplessness and in another we recognize tremendousness. They both exist. What a powerful duality.

Chapter Seven

LIVING IDEATION FOR WARRIOR SERVANTS

*Sometimes when you are in a dark place, you
think you have been buried, but actually,
you have been planted*
-Christine Caine

Living Ideation is a phrase I started using several years ago to describe my approach to mental health treatment. Living Ideation is an exploration of the thoughts and behaviors that make living better. It encourages us to see ourselves clearly and get in touch with our beliefs and feelings.

Most Warrior Servant populations think that some emotions shouldn't be talked about. For example, we don't usually share our feelings of guilt, fear, sadness, rage, and loneliness. Those are considered to be weak, and we won't let that be the truth. Avoid perceived weakness at all costs. Some emotions like joy, excitement, and love are acceptable to talk about. The simple truth is there are no good or bad emotions. There are only emotions, and we feel all of them. Emotions are truth. The tough part for Warrior Servants is they have a tough time allowing themselves to feel pain and sadness. Respectfully, it is time to get over ourselves and feel the truths that we all have in common.

We all feel the complexities of joy, despair, fear, and love. Therefore, it doesn't take a mental health professional to engage in the balancing act of mental health. Warrior Servants feel the same things as anyone else, and we are all in charge of navigating our emotions and relationships. These feelings impact who we are and who we interact with. We are all relatives, loved ones, friends, and colleagues to others. There is a responsibility to understand ourselves better so that we can steer our personal well-being, relationships, and careers in healthy directions.

We can connect with others in ways that help us become better. Mental health is about improving health and not repairing illness. Build not repair. Ideally, the concepts and approaches of Living Ideation would represent a return to cultural connectedness within our homes, schools, professions, and communities.

Most of the mental "health" programs within our organizations have focused on the warning signs of distress and danger. It makes sense to try and watch out for those in trouble, but we have been skipping the obvious opportunities to promote health and wellness. Here is the logic of Living Ideation for Warrior Servants: It is incredibly awkward, and rather ineffective, to jump right into heavy discussions about depression and dark thoughts. We should assess for health before we evaluate illness. The rationale for this approach is that we have to earn the right to "ask the hard questions." This is done within comfortable and safe relationships.

Living Ideation is not technique-driven, it is philosophy driven. It is a philosophy that acknowledges every one of us have successfully navigated 100% of our days. You're really good at problem-solving and there is no question about your ability to survive. You keep winning each day, and frankly, you haven't lost once. You keep persevering which means you know how to figure things out. Let's up your game.

Many reading this have interacted with others who have had dark thoughts. I'm sure you have too. Living Ideation reminds us that we can remember how we used to live; we can endure what is happening this day; we can plan how to live down the road when chaos has settled; we can dust off forgotten attitudes and create opportunities for present-day meaningfulness.

Why Do We Need a New Approach to Mental Health?

Mental health gets a bad rap within Warrior Servant cultures, and there have been too many stigmas associated with what mental health really is. Talking about emotions and the reality of the job is often considered weak. So many professions have believed that when someone is having trouble, they are automatically unfit for duty. What nonsense! Here's an example of how naïve some mindsets can be.

Dear John

John was a wet-behind-the-ears cadet from northern California, and it was mid-August at a base (not to be named) in the sweaty southern part of the country. He walked into the shrink's small office and had a seat. There was the door that he walked in and a door behind the doc. Between them, was a cold metal desk. Doc said, "What's going on?"

John began to describe that in his few weeks at BCT (Basic Combat Training), his favorite dog became ill and was put down. The kid also received a breakup letter from the girl of his dreams. He thought they were going to get married. To top it off, John also described how the grandmother who raised him was deteriorating and needed hospice care. The world outside of the Army was upside down.

The doc offered some words to John that normalized the pains of losing someone you grow up with (dog), losing the love of your life, and knowing your parent (grandparent) is dying. The kid was put back together and seemed to feel better after expressing his situation. As he walked out the same door he entered, two units were passing by in formation. John could see them glancing at him out of the corner of their eyes. What might they have been thinking as he walked out of the shrink's office?

Then the door behind the clinician opened and the CO (Commanding Officer) came in. The CO asked one question. "Is that kid fit for duty?" He didn't ask, "Who is that kid?" "Is he okay?" "How can I help?"

Dog. Love. Loss. The young man was experiencing the truths of young adulthood. Was he fit for duty? That's the wrong first question to ask. This young man was fit for the human experience. He was going through the paces of normal life, including many events that hurt like hell. This doesn't translate into being unfit for duty.

Warrior Servant cultures have many insulting stigmas about anxiety, depression, trauma, and suicide. Historically, we have discouraged our brothers and sisters from talking about things we all have in common. Let's set the record straight: Pain is not weakness. You are not soft for being overwhelmed. Having dark thoughts and considering suicide is not selfish.

We have all been told to soak up the good times and create memories that will be told for years. No doubt, your career is/has been/will be amazing! Many of us have also been discouraged from talking about the times that get under our skin. Bury the scary shit and get moving. Mission focus!

This culture of strength has influenced how we look after each other and assess pain. Most Warrior Servant professions only look for the warning signs of stress, depression, and suicide. Similar to the Dear John story, we have been influenced to only look for the warning signs of an impaired warrior.

The ways Warrior Servant professions typically assess for health have been perfectly backward. We look for what is wrong before we look for what is right. Additionally, we don't know what to do with our teammates when and if they are not doing well. For example, if you are taught the signs of depression, and you believe that your brother or sister is in trouble, what do you do with the information? "Hey, I'm worried about Johnny because he is withdrawn and drinking too much." Copy that. Johnny isn't pulling his weight. What the hell do you do now? Like many organizations, you either do nothing or you run it up the chain to someone in a supervisory role. Either way, Johnny is likely ignored or put under a microscope for further judgment. You forgot to lean in and remind Johnny that he is loved and not alone in his situation.

The common training programs and assessments for mental health can be helpful and effective. Unfortunately, they can trigger discomfort, hesitation, and non-participation from those who do not want to be perceived as weak. Warrior Servants will rarely admit to anything that could be considered less than awesome. They are reluctant to open the can-of-worms inside of their heads for the fear of not being able to put them all back inside. Therefore, many of you deflect those questions and conversations. Not too many want to "go there." Here's an example:

Supervisor: "Hey, brother. I'm worried about you. Have you been thinking of hurting yourself lately?"
"No, man. I'm okay. All good."
"You sure that you're good?
"Absolutely."
"Cool. If you need anything, let me know."

When we ask Warrior Servants to be honest about their pain, while they are wearing the armor of the job, they usually won't answer truthfully. The job requires calm and consistency, so they must push the true stress and chaos down somewhere. They are going to answer as a put-together professional who avoids being vulnerable. This pattern can be disastrous.

The Living Ideation approach unveils opportunities to talk with our loved ones and colleagues in more comfortable ways. When people feel more comfortable with conversations about their lifestyles and activities, they begin to build themselves up. Build rather than repair. Living Ideation conversations reveal health and stability.

Seeing yourself clearly is difficult to do, and most Warrior Servants default back to their careers. Remember the chapter about PT and MT? You know how to work hard and serve, but perhaps you have lost touch with the essence of who you really are. Your physical and professional training is dialed, but I'm willing to bet you have stopped doing some of the hobbies and activities that make you happy. I'm sure you have let some friendships and relationships fade as well. You have been so busy that you have lost track of what matters in your life. Your mental training has likely slipped quite a bit over the years.

Living Ideation approaches are focused on rediscovering who you are and what you are about. The following section is intended to be a high-intensity interval training (HIIT) workout for your headspace. Like your PT and professional skills, you will get out what you put in. When it becomes uncomfortable, you know that some changes are happening. This is where the magic happens. Keep going!

Please note: Living Ideation approaches are not intended to replace the utilization of competent mental health providers. The main objective of Living Ideation is to shift our conversations from being about risk reduction to growth and balance. Living Ideation conversations focus on health more than illness.

Chapter Eight

MENTAL HEALTH SIZE-UP

"On the mountains of truth, you can never climb in vain: either you will reach a point higher up today, or you will be training your powers so that you will be able to climb higher tomorrow."
– Friedrich Nietzsche

Living Ideation fits naturally with the warrior mentality of first responders, public service professionals, and military personnel. Quality mental health resources have been consistently developing for these populations, and they are sorely needed. Our communities ask more and more of our public servants while their resources are steadily diminishing. They are burning out. Actually, many of you are already smoked.

It is difficult to gather data describing the mental health struggles of military personnel, veterans, first responders, and those like them because these groups tend to keep their emotions close to the vest. Nonetheless, the little data that does exist has noted that our police, fire (structure and wildland), and military folks die by suicide more than they do within the line of duty (Centers for Disease Control, 2018; RAND, 2020). Chew on that for a moment. Our service members and first responders are more dangerous to themselves than their jobs are.

Trauma and traumatic exposures have a way of dominating a person's lifestyle. Relationships can turn sour. Job performance can deteriorate. At some point, health can take a nasty turn. Suddenly, life appears to have impenetrable darkness. Watching out for each other and keeping an eye on risky behaviors are appropriate, but please don't forget to recognize the fact that all of us have what it takes to be resilient and healthy. The vision of the Living Ideation approach for Warrior Servants builds upon the existing strengths of each warrior. Bottom line: we have all figured out how to get through every day that has led up to this moment. You are batting 1.000 in the game of life. You have skills and qualities that you don't give yourself credit for.

The bulk of your work lies in the ability to see yourself clearly. If you look in the mirror, what do you see? You may not like the person who is looking back at you. The Mental Health Size-Up offers appropriate questions to regularly think about. They will challenge you to reconnect with people and behaviors that matter the most. There are also two applications of a Peer Support model for folks in fire service and LE/Military. The brothers and sisters in other Warrior Servant professions can certainly identify with both versions.

Note to self: These questions might flex your brain in uncomfortable ways. That is part of the MT process. Mental training, like physical training, requires consistency. Some of your answers to the Size-Up questions might be "I don't know." Please allow your confusion to be the truth. That's the starting point of your growth. As you continue to ask the remaining questions, your brain will engage and begin dreaming about what is real and what is possible. Get to work!

Mental Health Size-Up

"Ask Yourself"

★ How do I separate Warrior and Self?

★ How do I maintain health?

★ What is my future vision?

★ What interests me?

★ How will I connect with others this week?

★ What are my financial objectives?

★ How will I prioritize meaningful relationships?

How do I separate Warrior and Self?

You are not simply the badass, get-it-done, warrior. You are more than a Soldier, Sailor, Airman, or Marine. More than a police officer. More than a firefighter. More than a dispatcher. More than a paramedic. Your abilities to concentrate and adapt translate into the other roles in life. Consider how you dial down the vigilant mindset of the warrior-self when you are not on duty and psychologically transition your energies into being a complete self. You may also be a partner, a sibling, a son/daughter, a hobbyist, etc. You were a self before you became a warrior; the warrior is now part of who you are; it is time to reclaim the self. Remember who you are and what you are about. When you find that this question is difficult to answer, please proceed to the other Size-Up questions. They will help you focus.

I separate Warrior and Self by

_____.

I separate Warrior and Self by

_____.

I separate Warrior and Self by

_____.

How do I maintain health?

This is not only physical health, nutrition, and diet. You train for physical fitness, and you train on apparatus and gear. Training on tactics and safety is the name of the game. Traditionally, we have not focused on training for mental health. Mental health is in stark contrast to illness, and we deserve to bolster our abilities for maximum effectiveness. Maintaining the instruments of your body and mind is fundamental to your lifestyle. Body. Spirit. Mind.

Perhaps you have dabbled with meditation and mindful exercises. This is a great example of a healthy practice. If any rifle hunters are reading this, you will recall the calm simplicity of having a buck in your sights: slow down, breathe, breathe, focus, breathe, squeeze. There are so many examples of health if you let your thoughts wander. Any thoughtful practice that settles the craziness of your world into a moment of peace is worth exploring more. Give it a try:

I maintain health when I

_____.

I maintain health when I

_____.

I maintain health when I

_____.

What is my future vision?

Here is the psychology behind this question: people who are in chronically depressed or suicidal headspaces can rarely describe their future. So, if you give yourself credit for making it this far in life, try to call your shot for a kick-ass future. This is about daydreaming and trying to focus on your opportunities.

People change as they get older. Our abilities change, our relationships change, and our careers change. What if you could steer those changes? You can. There aren't any rules in this exercise.

Imagine your personal and professional lifestyle in a few years. Who will you be? Perhaps you are having difficulty answering this question because your plate is overflowing with tasks and responsibilities. No problem! Asking yourself about the future puts you in a position to wonder and envision your possibilities. Now consider putting a few details and timelines into the dream.

Do you want to be in better shape? Fitness happens when you dial up a solid routine. Do you want to have a better relationship with your loved one? That will happen when you start to put a couple of ideas together. Do you want to hang out with your old buddies? I bet they would like to hang out with you too.

The fantastic movie, Space Balls has a great exchange: "When will then be now?" "Soon." The future is pretty much your call to make.

I want the future to have

_____.

I want the future to have

_____.

I want the future to have

_____.

What interests me?

This question should be the easiest to answer. The trick is to stop being so professionally awesome for a moment and reconnect with what floats your boat. Maybe you like hiking and fishing. Perhaps you haven't gone hunting or traveling to the coast in many years. If you love your dog, I imagine that he would burst at the opportunity to play fetch again. You get the point. Rekindle and maintain the hobbies and interactions that bring excitement, joy, and calm.

There is enough flavor in your life to brighten even the darkest of days.

I'm interested in

_____.

I'm interested in

_____.

I'm interested in

_____.

How will I connect with others this week?

This question is time oriented, and it asks for short-term detail. Commit to engagement with people outside of work. What do you have to lose besides a little bit of energy and some of your armor? Connectedness is a major factor for successful professionals who surge into health and wellness. We are all better together.

Please know that you are not the only one who has become over identified with work and the constant need to improve. The stress and anxiety that comes from your work are usually shoved down deep inside, and you likely tend to suffer in silence. What if you didn't keep things all to yourself? While you don't want your loved ones to know the gnarly details of your work, can they get a glimpse of how upsetting it can be? Will you respectfully get over yourself and let people around you know that your work is immensely gratifying, and it is also pretty damn hard?

Connecting with others isn't just about offloading your experiences. Being in honest relationships allows you the chance to decompress and be an authentic version of yourself. I hope you have people in your life who don't give two shits about what you do for a living. I hope you have people in your life who love you for simply being you. That is connectedness.

You are more than a Warrior Servant. Look back a few chapters and recall who your go-to people are. How will you maintain those bonds? The following spaces are for you to call your shot. Who will you connect with and what will you do? For example, I will connect with Chris and Justin by watching the Birds beat the Steelers this Sunday.

I will connect with/by

———————————————————————.

I will connect with/by

———————————————————————.

I will connect with/by

_____.

What are my financial objectives?

I wish this question wasn't necessary, but it is. While money doesn't buy happiness, country music has taught us that it can buy dirt, beer, and a fishing boat. Money can lead to a sense of stability, and stability can lead to brighter days. When you think about how you will spend your money and create stability, you are moving your life into the open seas. The options are limitless.

Thinking about money can be overwhelming. Do it anyway! Consider your financial goals so you can reach them. We all want that new fifth wheel or side-by-side to play with when we are on leave. Toys and adventures are awesome right up to the point of financial deficit.

Depending on how old you are, financial objectives change. The 23-year-old who banked over a thousand hours of OT might roll up in the new F-250. Cool rig, but did the dude think about the $792 payment for the next eight years? The 51-year-old might be thinking about mortgage payments, retirement accounts, and expenses associated with having two teenagers.

If you regularly size up your financial situation, then you are in control of your future. It doesn't matter how old you are or what your financial situation is. Today gets to be the day that you start leveling off the stressors associated with money. We all hope for a sense of predictability in life, and taking care of our financial future is a big part of the game.

My financial goal is

_____.

My financial goal is

_____.

My financial goal is

_____.

How will I prioritize meaningful relationships?

This question is the most important of them all. While it is true that you are born alone and will likely die alone, the rest of the journey is spent with other people. The quality of your relationships helps you stay healthy and successful in your career, and if you maintain those meaningful relationships, you will hopefully be surrounded by loved ones in your retirement years.

Some people are more special than others. You both deserve to recommit to each other. If you love someone, go love them. The varsity level of being in a solid relationship relies upon you allowing them to love you in return. Simple.

The art of having special relationships will be straightforward for Warrior Servants who are used to working hard. Think about the skillsets involved in PT and MT. If you apply the sincerity and enthusiasm you have for work to your personal life, you will surely find that those bonds improve over the years.

If your spouse or partner deserves more of your attention, think about how you can give it to them. If your kids aren't as close to you as they used to be, consider how to surprise them in new ways. If you haven't talked to your Pop in a while, imagine how to make him proud. Your friends are probably like family, and they deserve attention too. What could you do to grow those bonds?

Figuring out how to prioritize meaningful relationships is perhaps more essential than any of the other Mental Health Size-Up questions. The beauty lies within the exchange between you and another. When you communicate how important someone is, you improve their day. Like a boomerang, when their cup is full, they tend to return the gesture. Now your day has improved. Try jotting down a few thoughts.

Who is a special person and what will you do to make your relationship a bit better?

Who is my person and what will I do?

_____.

Who is my person and what will I do?

_____.

Who is my person and what will I do?

_____.

The Mental Health Size-Up asks questions that pertain to the person and not to the professional. Remember, you existed long before the professional did! You are a person before being a medic. You are a brother or sister before you are a firefighter. You are a son or a daughter more than you are a police officer. You are so much more than a military service member. The Living Ideation Mental Health Size-Up is geared for you to build upon the questions and philosophies of balance. The questions can shake you out of your atrophied mindset and move it into a lifestyle that has more meaning.

Chapter Nine

REAL PEER SUPPORT

"When you are in psychological distress and someone really hears you without passing judgment on you, without trying to take responsibility for you, without trying to mold you, it feels damn good!"

-Carl Rogers

Work stress and trauma affect everyone differently. How is it that some people are rarely fazed by awful experiences? They have an uncanny ability to let things slide off their back while their colleague wants to crawl into bed and cry. At some point in our careers, we will all be dropped to our knees, but typically, Warrior Servants are:

- Resistant/Immune: Some people aren't impacted by an event. They don't fall down often.
- Resilient: Some people are impacted, and they bounce back. They get up after they fall.
- Growth-oriented: Some people are impacted, and they get up and grow from the experience. They fall, get up, and improve.

When our brothers and sisters stay down for too long, they need help from their people. This is where you come in. You "get it" in ways that no one else does, and you are often more trustworthy than any clinician or outsider.

Many of you reading this belong to agencies and organizations that promote peer support. Perhaps, you already have a peer support team. Peer support has traditionally involved like-minded professionals who have gone through some fundamental training. These trainings, like the one offered through International Critical Incident Stress Foundation (ICISF), legitimize the philosophies and strategies for helping those in need.

Ideally, you would be knowledgeable and willing to support others effectively, but two things are stopping this development. First, you serve, but rarely allow people to serve you. Being honest about trauma can be hard to do. Second, our cultures haven't fully embraced being vulnerable and therefore we keep stigmatizing emotional pain and trauma.

Dr. Steven Silver, an addictions counselor who has worked with many veterans, coined the term Sanctuary Trauma. Our work environment is supposed to be emotionally safe, yet unfortunately, it can be more traumatizing than the job. So many service members and first responders do not feel comfortable talking about their traumatic injuries to others in their organization. I hope that we can loosen the knot of resistance and get back to the basics of being human. Vulnerability and humility are core concepts to real support among Warrior Servant populations.

The two images that follow describe the simple constructs of what real peer support should be. The first one uses military and law enforcement language, while the second mirrors an acronym familiar with fire culture. Regardless of your professional designation, these models apply to all of us. These peer support models are for anybody who strongly identifies with service. That could be a middle school teacher, daycare provider, stay-at-home parent, bus driver, etc.

Watch. Engage. Adapt. Support. These terms exemplify the common traits of someone who is constantly on duty. Someone in military service or para-military service is always watchful, ready to engage, prepared to adapt, and able to support. Apply those words to your profession. They fit. Watch. Engage. Adapt. Support.

My dear friend and colleague, Battalion Chief Derek Reid applied fire safety to the mental health of a fire crew. L.C.E.S. is a basic safety concept for wildland firefighters to protect themselves and those around them. It stands for Lookouts, Communications, Escape Routes, and Safety Zones. While being pretty self-explanatory, L.C.E.S. applies to almost everything in life. Have solid lookouts so that we can communicate consistently and effectively. Always know your escape routes to reliable safety zones. Live to fight the next fight!

Peer Support for Warrior Servants

WATCH

Be attentive. Notice any changes with your brothers and sisters. Allow them to do the same for you.

ENGAGE

Challenge with intent. Be authentic and thoughtful. Don't ask, "How are you doing?" Make statements that normalize the situation.

ADAPT

Move forward together to create a safe conversation and environment. Provide an outlet to communicate.

SUPPORT

Validate. Confirm their experiences. Listen much more than you talk.

Peer Support L.C.E.S.

LOOK OUTS
Be attentive for behavior changes. If something feels off about a peer, investigate.

COMMUNICATIONS
Challenge with compassion and supportive intent. Be authentic, empathize, validate, and confirm.

ESCAPE ROUTE
When you find a peer in crisis, meet them where they are. They will follow if they trust you.

SAFETY ZONE
Perception of judging or fixing too soon could turn a safety zone into a deployment site.

The tools for peer support remind everyone on a team to be attentive and engaged. The concepts promote consistent communications that are purposeful and authentic. People in first response culture know that trustworthiness is one of the key attributes to success. Stigmas will fade when conversations are supportive. Everyone must feel safe.

This is much easier said than done. Many organizations fall short when promoting and funding programs. Offering a telephone number with some support services is pathetic when outsiders are generally not welcome. We all know the best support comes from those who are on the inside. Until the culture evolves, please try to be part of the solution. This will involve understanding yourself and being able to create safe outlets for your brothers and sisters. Chief Reid said it best: "Within unity, we find strength."

Watch / Look Outs

Warrior servants are solid at having each others' backs. You know how to look out for one another. That's the easy part and it's in your blood. The hard part is, will you let your brother and sister have your back? Will you let them take care of you too?

Real peer support means that for as much as you watch out for me, you will let me watch out for you too. We won't be arrogantly strong, and we will allow ourselves to be called out. This fierce honesty must come with trust and there can't be fear of retaliation. This is why cultural change is key!

Pay attention to your brothers and sisters. Notice if their demeanor is changing. Perhaps they are burning out and need to tap out for a bit. Mistakes are usually avoidable and if we keep ourselves sharp, then we all gain.

Examples:

"My crew has been on for 8 days in a row. They are toast."

"My shift lead has been a jerk and a half this week. Something's up."

"My partner has been really quiet today. That's not her style."

Again, you are probably great at watching out for others. Can you let others do the same for you?

Engage / Communications

Recall a time you were in the middle of a gnarly call full of adrenaline and action. Maybe it was a multi-casualty event or a near-death experience. What if I happened to cross paths with you as it was wrapping up and I said something like, "Hey, how's it going? You doing okay?" What would you say?

Engagement might not be what you think it is. If you are like most people, you tend to ask questions like the ones I did. At face value, these are thoughtful and appropriate. Unfortunately, many of you won't answer these questions honestly. You won't answer because the questions reawaken the public servant. You are sparked into a mode that is on duty and not willing to talk about what happened. Questions trigger people to put on the armor and be "hard." When you're amped and in go-mode, you will probably respond by saying, "I'm fine. Okay. Good." I've come to recognize that "fine" is about halfway between fucked up and awesome. We deserve better.

Effective communication starts with noticing changes in behaviors and the environment. Remember the first step is to Watch/Look Out. When we see something is off, we engage and speak to the truth of the moment. Peer Supporters allow the truth of a moment to be exactly what it is, and we try not to ask questions that will get fake answers.

Team cohesion depends on steady communication. This is especially true in times of stress and hardship. Most of our effective communications are statements about the truth rather than questions that can be dodged with false strength. It's okay to not be okay!

Examples:
"Hey, buddy. That was a tough call tonight. I'm smoked."

"No one should see what we just did. Let's get some chow and decompress."

"You haven't been your usual self lately. I'm worried about you."

"I miss home."

"I'm so sick of Gatorade."

"I've never done something like that before and I hope I never have to again."

"That was FUBAR."

Again, when you ask silly questions to a person who is professionally engaged, you're going to get lied to. They are in work mode and not feel mode. Instead, use statements that are authentic, real, and confirm what the person is probably going through. If it's been an awful event, it's appropriate to say that it was awful. Peer support communications are simply validating statements. They're not silly questions. When you make a statement that is close to the truth, you will see your brothers and sisters bobble-heading as if they heard the truth for the first time. You will be able to speak for them and then you can move forward as a team.

Adapt / Escape Route

The road to a healthier culture relies on the existence of many like-minded people. These peer supporters have two basic traits: Trust and commitment. Who are the trustworthy people in your organization who are also committed to helping others? Are you one of those people? You can be.

Leaders aren't solely at the top of the org chart, and peer supporters can exist at all levels of your team. Your Chief should be able to still connect with the probie who is experiencing things for the first time. Similarly, the new kid should be taught how to have empathy for others too. Peer support ideally works horizontally and vertically through the ranks.

Here is where words turn into actions. When you determine that your peer is in a tough spot, create a comfortable and safe moment to talk about things. Remember, don't ask stupid questions because they won't get truthful responses. If you are a trusted comrade, they will follow your lead toward calmer times. If they trust you, they will follow you.

Examples:
"Let's finish this line and get back down the hill for some water and rest. We need to dial back."
"That last call was awful. Let's sit for a bit and walk it through so we can get some sleep tonight."

"You have taken quite a few OT shifts lately. I think that you are burning out and could use some time away from this noise."

Support / Safety Zone

The overall objective of supporting each other is to create a healthier culture. Imagine a supportive profession that encourages you to kick ass and achieve results while also normalizing the emotional tolls that are paid. This will take time, and it will be worth the effort. More Warrior Servants will have long careers and even longer retirements.

Safety zones need to reduce the over-stimulating stressors of the job. Sometimes this type of support can be a cup of coffee and a few minutes to decompress. Other times a Hawaiian vacation is appropriate. Safety zones and supportive environments might include your loved ones, your backyard, or the carburetor that you are rebuilding for your '83 CJ-7.

Recognize that the season or shift will eventually transition to the other facets of your life. There is leave in between deployments. Use it! Safety zones are not band-aids; they are comfortable moments and behaviors that can offer balance.

Examples:

"We're almost off shift. You want to grab your wife
    and kids and meet us at the lake?"

"I'll take care of the paperwork. Do you mind
    grabbing some sandwiches for the two of us?"

"We've been grinding for a week. Let's dial back the
    non-essentials for a few days."

The basic approach to Living Ideation for peer supporters is simple. In truth, most of us have known these principles for many years, yet we have forgotten how to check in with others. The basic tenets of true peer support are below.

- Ask people about themselves.
- Listen like you care about them.
- Expand upon purpose and meaning.
- Stay connected with them and let them stay connected with you.

Creating a Peer Support program

It doesn't take too much time to recognize that your work leaves a residue of impact. The job changes people. If you can recognize the trauma and drama of being a Warrior Servant, then you have been paying attention, and you have an opportunity to act. If you choose to do nothing with your stress, then you will most likely suffer the consequences of your health and relationships. If you try to wash off the residue, then you stand to gain in countless ways.

You may not know how to reset and recharge. Perhaps you think that you are stuck. Well, you aren't alone, and you don't need to be alone in this chaos. Your colleagues might see you more clearly than you see yourself, and they can help you get back to basics. This is why having a culture of peer support is so important.

Not too long ago, Warrior Servant cultures looked down upon those who expressed emotions. We have come a long way, and there is still far to go. Peer support programs are becoming a common part of the first responder world, and our men and women are better for it. The benefits of being aware and helping each other far outweigh the consequences of naïvely keeping our heads in the sand. We talk about things now and the goals of providing emotional support are here to stay. Starting a peer support program isn't daunting, and it is quite straightforward. There are two core principles: Competence and trust.

<u>What makes a good peer supporter?</u>

Think about the people you work with. Some are dependable and some are easy to avoid. Simply, your peer support team should be a diverse collection of go-to professionals. These are the individuals who are damn good at their job, they never quit training, and they are respected throughout the organization. Search your head. Who are three people who embody professionalism, improvement, and respect?

Ideal Peer Supporter:

_____.

Ideal Peer Supporter:

_____.

Ideal Peer Supporter:

_____.

What to include in a peer support program?

A Peer Support program is much more than the people who step up to the challenge. A program includes the organizational pieces to stay afloat and to continually improve. Here are a few to consider:

- Peer team leaders: Depending on the size of your organization, there should be at least two peer team leaders. The direction of the organization should never rest on a single person's shoulders.

- Team members throughout the ranks: Peer team members should come from all levels of the organization. This includes senior leadership, veteran employees, retirees, younger generations, and even up-and-coming probies.

- Continuing education and training: Warrior Servants never stop training, neither does a Peer Support team. Peer team members and leaders of an organization must continue to stay sharp. Peer support courses and refreshers can be implemented throughout the year. Role plays and scenarios are included in all training.

- Money: Peer Support teams need to be funded to ensure a stable program is in place. Agencies and organizations should prioritize the mental health and wellness of their members by putting Peer Support in their budgets.

- Rotation of roles: Train and transition the leadership within the program. Level out the talent and expand the culture.

What are the ethics and rules for a peer support program?

Confidentiality and discretion are obviously part of the team's responsibilities. Many states have legal protections for Peer Support team communications that apply to almost all interactions. Look up the statutes and keep them handy in case administration or Human Resources wants you to spill your beans. The only exceptions to confidentiality are if the employee is a danger to themselves or others. Otherwise, your role is to be discreet.

The main goal for a team is to create a culture that is accepting and supportive of health. We want our brothers and sisters to know we are here to help. Keep it simple by establishing a team that is trustworthy and dedicated to their work-family.

Clinicians who are worth their salt.

Some organizations and agencies have mental health clinicians who are either embedded or accessible. Not all shrinks are created equal, and there are two fundamental criteria that a Warrior Servant clinician needs to have: Cultural competency and trauma training.

If you were looking for a clinician to work out your darkness and pain, you would want to know if the person had any experience working with people like you. If they have experience treating people in your line of work or similar professions, then you can begin to trust them. Trust in their experience is huge!

You also need to know if the therapist is trauma-informed and trained to work with traumatic injuries. Warrior Servants eat trauma for breakfast, lunch, and dinner. You deserve a mental health provider who is well-trained. Solid therapists don't rescue people; they help others rescue themselves.

Speed to trust.

My friend Jeremy spent a pile of time in the Army and wildland fire. He mentioned a concept called Speed to Trust and how it applied to outsiders. It especially applied to mental health clinicians who worked with Warrior Servant populations. Here is what he said,

"Speed to trust is an unspoken social skill needed to be successful and effective in a dynamic environment with unknown personalities and skillsets. Wildland firefighters commonly find themselves in a fire situation with new groups and entities that they need to trust to accomplish a common goal. The quicker they can build trust, the quicker they can get on the same page and accomplish these quickly evolving challenges. Individual fire qualifications and assigned units are a start but the trust quickly improves with clear and effective communication. The actions taken or not taken with this communication builds trust and successful outcomes. Speed is relative to the communicators' understanding of this. Performance is implied, trust is not."

Performance is implied; trust is not. That hits the nail on the head and applies to a team of peers, leaders, admin, and clinicians.

Prevention and Suppression

Firefighting professionals and many Warrior Servants know the differences between prevention and suppression. Peer support programs focus on ways to support the health of their membership while being ready to help with challenging events. We do not wait for critical events to spark us into action; we keep watch over our brothers and sisters and maintain relationships that have emotional intimacy.

Peer support teams strive to know the membership on deeply personal levels. Connectedness allows people to intervene well before major problems develop. Depression, Anxiety, Trauma, and substance use disorders can be managed and helped before the consequences of a damaged career, ruined relationships, and poor health.

Chapter Ten

WARRIOR SERVANTS AND RELATIONSHIPS

"When we feel generally secure, that is, we are comfortable with closeness and confident about depending on loved ones, we are better at seeking support - and better at giving it."
-Sue Johnson

This is going to get a little awkward. Sit quietly for a moment and ask yourself, "What's it like to be in a relationship with me?" This is you versus yourself and I hope that you can reflect honestly. There is nothing to lose here, and you have much to gain by growing your perspective. What's it like being on the receiving end of your actions?

Recall the primary roles you have and be honest about those relationships. For example, I am a husband, father, friend, and mental health professional. I travel frequently for work, and it takes a toll on all of us. It is probably lonely for my wife, and I know that she didn't sign up to be a single parent. My kids run the risk of growing up without a present father figure. My friends and colleagues tend to get a distracted version of me. I don't spend as much quality time with my favorite people, and therefore, I need to consider how I can make the most of my opportunities. I can lean in and make some changes. I can make my moments with them count towards happiness and fulfillment.

In chapter four, you were introduced to the concept of Battle Rhythm and how the Warrior Servant tends to run at a break-neck pace while ignoring many important people and lifestyles. The recognition of this rhythm is important. Below, you will see an illustration of a common example. The graph shows that almost all energy is spent as the Warrior Servant. Stephen King noted, "All work and no play, makes Jack a dull boy."

Battle Rhythm of the Warrior Servant

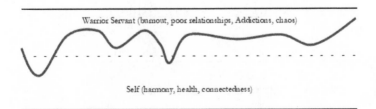

Warrior Servant (burnout, poor relationships, Addictions, chaos)

Self (harmony, health, connectedness)

If you can become more aware when you are over identified as the Warrior Servant, you can then make some changes to your pace of play. You can prioritize the roles and relationships that matter in the long run. Do you regularly grind in the top half and ignore your personal life? If so, consider the second chart that has a flow between the Warrior and the self.

Illustration of balanced rhythm

Battle Rhythm of the Warrior Servant

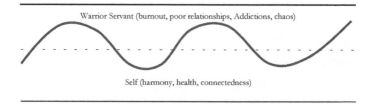

Warrior Servant (burnout, poor relationships, Addictions, chaos)

Self (harmony, health, connectedness)

Your turn. Try to answer the following questions. Be honest with yourself and then make a plan for improvement.

What's it like <u>to be in a partnership/marriage</u> with me?

_____.

How can I improve my relationship?

_____.

What's it like <u>to be related</u> to me?

_____.

How can I improve my relationship?

_____.

What's it like <u>to work</u> with me?

_____.

How can I improve my relationship?

_____.

What's it like <u>to be friends</u> with me?

_____.

How can I improve my relationship?

_____.

What's it like <u>to be by myself</u>?

_____.

How can I improve my relationship with myself?

_____.

I bet you were able to offer a quick response to some of those questions, and I hope some of your relationships are positive and healthy. If any of the questions gave you pause, please dig into them a bit more. Your battle rhythm is likely out of sync. The key to your improvement is to harness the ability to see yourself clearly.

The last question has some teeth, and it is intended to shake your perspective. What is it like to be by yourself? How good of a company are you to yourself? If you tend to treat others better than you treat yourself, please know that you are not alone. That's what over identified Warrior Servants do. You serve! You serve until your life becomes unmanageable. Please look at those questions again and make a note that describes how you can improve each relationship. Nothing to lose. All to gain.

Living Ideation: Connect with your "Family"

It should be noted that this section uses a term that might not fit for some. "Family" should not necessarily apply to people whom you share blood with, because some families are garbage. We don't all get the same start in this life, nor do we all get to have supportive people around us when we are young. Family describes those we choose to be in our lives.

Your family is the varsity team of people who add vibrancy to your life.

The following tool was originally developed to be used as a pre- and post-deployment model for military service members. It applies to all Warrior Servants. It is meant to help jumpstart and maintain connections with loved ones. As you read, imagine applying the topics to yourself, and then think about using them with your family. You deserve to improve your understanding of your loved ones, and this will take a bit of effort. If you find that your relationships are going down the tubes, then the risk factors and warning signs serve as reminders to ask for more help.

The talking points are organized in a way that guides you toward a better understanding of your family member. Like the Mental Health Size-Up, there aren't any right or wrong answers. There are simply your answers, and if you can't come up with anything, then that's your truth at the moment.

The amazing work of Dr. Sue Johnson is a strong influence on this exercise. Johnson suggests that we have basic needs in an adult relationship. Each person needs to have a sense that they are:

- Lovable
  - Am I lovable to you?
- Valuable
  - Am I valuable to you?
- Competent

- Am I good at being in this relationship with you?

You and your family member need to know that they are more than loved and valued; you are deserving of being loved and valued. Additionally, we all need to know that we are capable in our roles. We need to know that we are good at being in our relationships and we matter to others.

If the answers to the Connect with your Family instrument come easily to you, then engage with the information. If not, then get curious about your loved one and try to know them better. Do you have anything to lose by trying to connect with your people in new ways? Nope.

Living Ideation Connect with your family	Risk Factors When to ask for help
Daily engagement with your family: Can you answer these questions about each family member? • What is exciting for them? • What are they good at? • What are they proud of? • What are they looking forward to? • Who do they like to spend time with? Conversation topics: • What is something enjoyable that you can do today? • What did you appreciate today? • What was interesting today? • Tell your family member what you love about them today. • Describe what your family member did well today.	Notice changes in your loved one: ▲ Loss of interest in activities or having fun ▲ Loss of energy or tired all the time ▲ Feelings of low confidence, thinking they can't do anything well ▲ Feeling confused or unable to think clearly ▲ Statements about killing themselves Look for opportunities every day to connect with your family members, keeping in mind the Living Ideation conversation topics. If you see any of the risk factors listed above, reach out for more support.

The materials recommend <u>daily</u> engagement with each other. Notice that the frequency is <u>daily</u>. This routine is intended to create a new habit for you and your family. Similar to PT and MT, if you connect with your family on a regular basis, you will be fit. Family fitness, like many skills, can be perishable. It will fall out of shape and getting your fitness level back can be painful. If we are having Living Ideation conversations, we are consistently dialing in with each other. We are connecting! Then we can maintain those connections. Give the following questions some thought.

- What is exciting for your family member?
  It is quite likely that the people in your family get energized in ways that are different from you. Try to recognize how they are motivated. These concepts are like everlasting batteries to their lifestyles.

  Examples:
  "She lights up every time she is with her friends."
  "He can't get enough time camping. He never wants to come home."
  "My kiddo loves having time to play online with friends."
  "He picks out a different jersey for each Sunday game."

- What is your family member good at?
  Self-esteem improves when one has a sense that they are proficient in life. When we recognize the many talents of our family members, we can consistently fill their cups with value.

  Examples:
  "My son is a master at his video game."
  "My daughter has a better cross-over than any other kid on the court."
  "My partner is an amazing artist."
  "My Battalion Chief is one hell of a hunter."

- What is your family member proud of?
  When your sense of self is full, your identity and life likely have stability. If you can recognize what your people are proud of, you are in a terrific position to lean in and expand on what is already working. It is a simple way to promote what they love. Please note that what you're proud of them for may or may not be what they are proud of themselves for. Get to know your loved ones!

  Examples:
  "My husband runs at least one marathon a year."
  "My work buddy made fishing flies for the entire department."
  "My mom volunteers 20 hours a week for the local VA."

- What does your family member look forward to?
  Future orientation is an indicator that someone is not permanently stuck in a dark mindset. Hopefulness can translate into compass headings for future growth and happiness.

  Examples:
  "My crew mate wants to become a pilot in the next few years."
  "Being a probie sucks! He's looking forward to getting signed off and moving forward."

"She is so stoked to retire in 36 months. She wants to travel around Asia."

The questions are for you and not the other person. This is key! If you can answer the questions about your family member, then you are likely in sync. If you pause and need to reflect, then there is some work to do. No problem. This tool is a conversation starter.

The bottom portion of the left side has specific topics that you can build on. When people are describing what they are doing in the future, the situation is starkly different from being burnt out and cynical. Thinking about the future and staying connected gives loneliness and anger competition. Warrior Servants tend to be pretty hardcore and they like being competitive. Use that competitiveness and be more connected with your relationships. Try to get those you care about to describe themselves more. This will help you know how to make your best moves. The following conversation topics are designed with connectedness in mind.

- What is something fun you have planned in the next day or two?
  Get specific! When a person can articulate detailed plans of living, they tend to focus their energies on the event.

Examples:
"I'm going to go paddleboarding when I get off shift."
"I want to sleep in and then watch a movie on Saturday."
"If I can finish this pile of paperwork, I want to play basketball with the fellas."
"I want to get in the workshop and decompress."

- What did you laugh about today?
  Humor is a sign that a person is happy, and there is a ton of research describing the health benefits that come from laughter. Dust off the cheesy dad jokes and give them a whirl. It feels good to laugh, and it feels even better to help others smile. These comments can be opportunities to share fun experiences.

  Examples:
  "My friend knows how to do the best impressions of our Sergeant."
  "We threw quarters for dishes last shift. You should have seen Cap's face when he lost."
  "When I got home, the dog almost knocked me over with excitement.

- What was interesting today?

  These responses will prove to be amazing conversation starters. What a simple way to engage and maintain thoughtful connections!

  Examples:

  "My buddy asked me to imagine how I would run the department if I were in charge."

  "I noticed the cool air on my run this morning. I think Fall might come early."

  "I saw an osprey pull a fish out of a lake today. It was really cool."

- Tell your people what you love about them today.

  This idea is statement based rather than a question. Relationships can fall out of shape if they aren't maintained. It is hard to believe that anyone would grow tired of hearing kind and authentic things about them. What you put out to others comes back at you in amazing ways.

  Examples:

  "I can't get enough of your smile and laugh."

  "Hanging out with you was the best part of my day."

  "You see things in ways I never have. I love that about you."

  "You inspire me."

- Describe what your family member did well today. Do not offer false praise. Focus on the things that make your family member special. This allows everybody to be individuals and not clones. Our differences make life interesting.

  Examples:
  "You kept at it on the court today. I could tell that your team was inspired by your persistence."
  "I know that I have been gone a lot lately. You have really picked up my slack and kept us afloat."
  "There is no way that I could pull this off without you. You have skills that I can't seem to figure out."
  "You contribute so much to our team. You make our job easier."
  "You wake up earlier than most people do. That takes dedication!"

The questions and comments suggest that each person in your life is successful in many things. They have so much talent and ability. Fun exists. Laughter exists. Life is interesting. They are loved and appreciated. They do things well.

The Living Ideation Connect with your Family interview consistently tries to highlight the strengths within people. The model assumes that everyone has the ability to grow and improve. The conversations can apply to people in your families, your careers, and in your social circles. The main goal of this approach is to strengthen the relationships that help you be the best version of yourself.

How to interact with your people: Junior Varsity Counseling skills

Warrior Servants are good at taking care of others, and they tend to work themselves to exhaustion. There are consequences when you prioritize making a difference in the world, and the price is usually close to home. Have you ever heard the question, "Why do we always hurt the ones we love the most?" The answer is simple: Because you can. You can get away with being short-tempered, unprofessional, and inappropriate with your closest people because they won't write you off…. until they do.

If you scream at your superior, you won't get to work there very long. If you get shitty with your friends, they won't be your friends much longer. If you do those things to your family members, they will probably put up with it for a long time. You have more fuse length with your inner circle of people, and it takes many painful experiences for that bomb to go off.

You don't need to be a professional counselor to know how to be effective in relationships. The basic skills are straightforward and you can master them quickly. The three principles that can help you improve your relationships come from Carl Rogers. Rogers was one of the founding fathers of psychotherapy and his approach is called Person-Centered Therapy. It's also referred to as a humanistic approach.

Humanism boils down to being more self-aware and thoughtful of others. In a perfect world, that wasn't full of trauma and chaos, being calm and healthy would be easy. Unfortunately, in the Warrior Servant's world, life gets pretty tangled up. Below is a graphic that shows the fundamentals Rogers applied to all relationships.

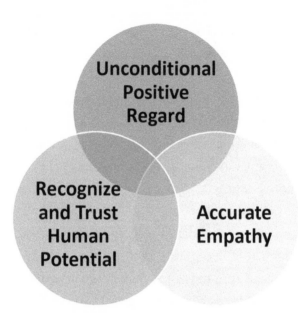

Out of all the collateral duties that we have in life, being in loving relationships is the best one. If your upbringing was harsh or you have been treated poorly, you may not know how to treat people well. Here's the simple rule: Treat them like you actually care about them! The three intertwined circles are the junior varsity counseling skills that will help your relationships reach new heights.

<u>Unconditional Positive Regard</u>

Many Warrior Servants treat the general public with grace and respect. There aren't conditions on their commitment to providing aid. You sacrifice unconditionally, especially when you are mission focused. This path can be taken with those in your personal life too.

Do you love your spouse or partner? Of course, you do. Does your loved one ever mess up in life? Yep! Hopefully, we all get permission to make mistakes. Unconditional positive regard means that you can accept people in the good times and the bad times. It assumes that people try to do the best they can with what they have. If you can apply this principle to your close circle of people, then there aren't many things we can't figure out.

Examples:

"I know that things didn't go as planned. I'm glad to be home with you."

"You tried your best, and I appreciate the effort."

"I love you."

"I don't care who won the game. I like watching you play."

"Even if we could go back and try again, it wouldn't change how I feel about you."

Accurate Empathy

Many of you have empathy for the people you serve. You help those in need, and you can imagine being in their shoes. Step that up quite a bit and wonder what it is like being your loved one. Now try to be as specific as possible with empathy. Remember the philosophy of real peer support is to talk with someone accurately. Don't ask lame questions like, "how are you doing?" Make statements that are close to the mark. If you can make an accurate statement about what is going on, I bet the connection between you and the other person gets better. It means that you "get it."

Examples:

"That's awesome! You worked so hard for that promotion."

"I've been gone a long time. You learned how to run this family without me."

"I wish you didn't have to go through that. It sounds awful."

"The loss still gets to you. He meant so much."

"You were patient, and it didn't work out. I'd be upset too."

Recognize and Trust Human Potential

Do you think people can change? If you are still reading this book, I sure hope that you think change is possible! The core belief of growth is essential to having great relationships. None of us are the same as when we were younger, and, if we pay attention, we level up throughout our life. We're supposed to change, and when we have people who believe in our potential, we can accomplish amazing things.

Now turn the tables and apply this idea to your loved ones. Relationships get stuck when there is a sense of judgment and mistrust. This is a recipe for loneliness. Can you recognize and trust the potential in others?

Examples:

"That was so close. If you could try that one more time, I think you would nail it."

"Your fitness goals are ambitious. Go for it!"

"Of course, I think you can do it."

"We can figure this out together."

"Please don't quit. I believe in you."

We are all in this game together, and we all bring different qualities to the table. If we can embrace the challenges as much as we welcome the victories, then we are headed in the right direction. Your relationships can become more authentic and rewarding when you:

- Accept them unconditionally
- See them clearly
- Believe in them when they don't believe in themselves

Please give yourself credit for being able to help your brothers and sisters. If you can slow down and unconditionally accept people for who they are, you will realize that most of the time, people make sense. This understanding can grow into an ability to have grace and compassion. We all can grow in new ways.

Chapter Eleven

Time To Hang It Up
Retiring Happily Ever After

"The harder you work, the harder it is to surrender."
-Vince Lombardi

Your career pays you financially and will hopefully set you up with a predictable retirement, yet Warrior Service is bigger than the paycheck. It's more of a calling. This calling rises up within you and it is apparent in every aspect of your life. When the time comes when you can discharge from your duties, what happens to the calling? How will you leave the shield and armor at the door of retirement? You are retiring from your career in service, but what are you about to begin?

You have opportunities to grow and improve upon the person who made it this far. This book has encouraged you to focus on your health and strengths; your transition into retirement is no different. If that sounds too simple, consider a basic philosophy of a combat diver: Plan your dive and dive your plan. Call your shot and execute.

Call Your Shot
Your Personal Wellness Guide

You work hard being productive and accountable. Your time can be healthy and restorative. Here are several questions to help you on your way.

- How do I describe myself outside of warrior service?
- Who will I spend time with that isn't a work buddy?
- What will I be doing that is meaningful outside of service?
- What will I learn about when I'm not working?
- How will I stay emotionally and physically healthy?
- How will I stay connected with my loved ones?
- How will I stay connected with my service family?

You deserve to live a life outside of service that is genuine and full. This is a guide for describing your relationships, hobbies, and growth opportunities, outside of your career. Look it over a couple of times and let your mind wander toward the people and activities that make you whole. I imagine some of your retirement will include your brothers and sisters in arms. Many people stay connected with their colleagues, but remember that you are so much more than the Warrior Servant.

The Call Your Shot guide is another opportunity for you to be a full-functioning human. Use the following spaces to take the armor off and describe your plan for health.

How do I describe myself outside of warrior service?

_____

_____

_____

Maybe you are in a significant relationship or are part of a close-knit family. Are you a person of faith? Do you have any hobbies? Who are you without service?

At some point, your answer might be, "I have no idea who I am outside of my career." That awareness is key to moving forward in a meaningful way. "I don't know," is your answer and the starting point for the amazing things to come.

Who will I spend time with that isn't a work buddy?

_____

_____

_____

Warrior Servants don't have too many people in their lives who "get it," and it is understandable that you haven't socialized outside of work with normies and civilians. The problem with only hanging out with people who wear similar uniforms is you can't thoroughly shake the experiences of the job. I'm pretty sure that when you stand around the Traeger with work folk, you find yourselves talking shop. Your retirement years should have stories of your past, comforts of the present, and unwritten adventures. If you can create a larger circle that includes friends who weren't in service, then you will likely be talking about things other than PT routines, .556, insomnia, toilet paper, etc.

What will I be doing that is meaningful outside of service?

_____

_____

_____

Active service provides many years of undeniable worth, and there is a concrete understanding that what you do truly stands for something important. As retirement sets in, you can look back and know your career stood for strength, honor, reliability, and duty. It was easy to see those valiant traits when you were kicking ass in your career, but it can be difficult to transition your skillsets into your personal life in ways that create meaningfulness.

Think about the ideas of strength, honor, reliability, and duty. The job didn't give you those traits. They came from within you. They are the fabric of who you are, and that's why you will be able to create activities full of meaning and purpose.

What will I learn about when I'm not working?

_____

_____

_____

Earlier in the book, you were encouraged to be a beginner in life. That means you will need to stop being in charge of every moment. If your career pushed you towards being a perfectionist, who knows how to do everything, then you most likely applied those traits to your personal life. Retirement will be pretty uncomfortable if you keep going down the same path. Stop being so awesome!

There is so much to learn in life, and now that you have more time, you get to jump into the deep end of things that interest you. If you like turning a wrench on cars, now you get to use the tools that you have accumulated over the years. If you like to hunt and fish, you are in a position to approach the craft in new ways. You want to explore the world? Pull out some maps and start daydreaming about all the places you are curious about. This is your window to grow.

How will I stay emotionally and physically healthy?

_____

_____

_____

_____

_____

There are a couple of extra lines for this question because it is incredibly important for you to focus on your emotional and physical health. Let's face it, Warrior Servants don't live nearly as long as they should because they have injuries, exposures, addictions, and broken relationships. You deserve to have a retirement that is at least as long as your career, and the only way that is going to happen is if you call your shot.

No one is going to hand you a kick-ass life on a platter. It is your responsibility. The section about PT and MT is worth another glance. If you can create routines for your physical training and enhance the opportunities for mental training, then you can surge into an exciting future. Seriously, you earned this! Take it!

How will I stay connected with my loved ones?

_____

_____

_____

Think back to how many family photos you aren't in. Santa didn't always come down the chimney on the 25th and your anniversary was often celebrated on a different date. Holidays and important events were flexed to another day because you were on shift. You don't get to redo the past, but you can wrap your head around all the new opportunities with your loved ones.

Now that you aren't beholden to your agency or Uncle Sam, start imagining how nice your time with your loved ones can be. Your relationships are surely going to benefit when you take the time to prioritize them. Now you get to do so many things together that were put on hold for so many years. Bonus: As you learn to connect with your loved ones better, they will be learning how to connect with you too.

How will I stay connected with my service family?

_____

_____

_____

No one gets left behind. Retirement can be lonely, and downright shitty, for those who don't have healthy relationships and lifestyles. Warrior Servants have a tendency to bond with each other in ways that they don't with their family and friends. It makes sense on many levels. When the career comes to an end, many of those ties come loose, and our service family can wither away.

This is where you come in. You can take the initiative and stay connected with your brothers and sisters. You know that you still need them because they "get it" in ways no one else does. Take it to the bank that they need you too. I want you to think harder about this part of the Call Your Shot assignment. This is more than calling once in a while or getting together for some beers. It is bigger than the annual camping trip. How will you stay connected on deep and soulful levels?

The Grand Daddy of all After Action Reviews

Retirement from a career in service will be heavy. It should be. If you put your heart and energy into your time, you will likely be in a place that is awkward and weirdly quiet. You are in a position to reflect upon who you have been and who you get to be in the future. The Call Your Shot is simply an After-Action Review of your personal life, relationships, and opportunities. Please smile and know that you have earned every step of your life up to this point. You made it! Proceed with intention.

Chapter Twelve

STORIES OF WARRIOR SERVICE

"Go do. Do things that excite you. Things that inspire you. Things that challenge you, stretch you, fuel you, fulfill you, and make you feel grateful to be alive."
-Lori Deschene

I have sat with many vulnerable and courageous Warrior Servants throughout the years, and I am honored to walk with them through darkness. The following stories describe their willingness to confront trauma and pain while uncovering untapped abilities to create newness. It should be noted that all names and identifying information have been changed.

Trauma happens to all Warrior Servants throughout their careers, and it changes them. There are a handful of undeniable events that hit hard because they are lived experiences. There are also countless indirect exposures to suffering and despair. The following tales from the couch illustrate how terrible events and trauma can yield amazing untapped potential for health and beauty.

These vignettes all have several concepts in common, and you will recall them from the discussion about Charlie Brown. Warrior Servants, like Charlie Brown, experience times when they think that they don't fit in with the gang (work and family); life is all pain all the time; they think they have lost their sense of purpose and achievement.

The key principles of Living Ideation help each warrior realize the potential to rediscover or create new moments that are curious and powerful. Each story will illustrate newfound senses of belonging, non-pain, and achievement. The lessons learned will be listed at the end of each vignette.

The First First Responder: Dispatch

When people hear the phrase, "first responder," they usually think of cops, firefighters, and paramedics. Dispatch workers are often overlooked and forgotten about. In truth, dispatchers are the first First Responders. When someone calls 911, dispatchers take the brunt of the initial chaos and horror of an event. Imagine the toll that would take on a person.

The following conversation describes how an exceptional dispatch coordinator had to confront the reality that her career and personal life were intertwined. She and I met for quite a few sessions, and this is a compressed version of our hours together.

"Charlene, I'd like to know more about what you have been going through."

"Call me Shar. I'm a dispatcher and I am not long for this career. It's too much. It's too much death, screaming, and stupid people. I'm fucking exhausted."

Of course, her work is too much. Dispatchers are a special breed, and they wear a bit of every call. At some point, it is too heavy. "Shar, when I imagine what you do for a living and how you put yourself in the center of people's worst moments, I am short of breath."

Shar looked at me directly for the first time and said, "If you only knew the images and sounds that go through my head."

"When you are stuck in those moments, I bet there are some calls playing on repeat. Tell me one that sticks to you more than others." I imagined that there was a straw that broke the camel's back, and she would have a vivid story queued up.

She paused for a long while before she began. "I take bad calls every day, and I am pretty good at being calm and professional. It's the job. I actually like being the one who is in the position to help someone when they are going through hell." She stopped talking and looked at the plant on my desk.

I threw a straight pitch. "What happened, Shar?"

"It was my dad."

This could go a few different ways, but clearly, this was going to be a deep wound. A complicated one. I waited for her to continue as she stared at the plant on my desk. She slowly shook her head in disbelief and said, "It was a traffic accident where a woman was trying to quiet her baby and she took her eyes off the road. She drifted into the other lane and hit a 2002 silver F-150. It was my dad."

I waited and leaned forward in my chair a bit. Shar's recollection of the truck was precise. Of course, it was. She had probably been in it many times. The silence was so loud and all I could think was, "Holy shit! This woman dispatched the accident that killed her father."

I eventually told her that I wanted to hold some of the pain with her and that our space was a safe place to process it. She unloaded. "Kids aren't supposed to die, and that fucking lady was the only survivor. She killed her kid, and she killed my dad with her stupidity! I was on the line, gathering as much information as possible, and I find out it is my dad. How the fuck does that happen?"

I wanted to move at her pace, so I let the truth and disbelief set in. When she made eye contact with me, I asked, "What was the hardest part of that day?" This was a question intended to get her grounded in the confusion.

Clearly, she had thought about this. She understood that there were two families impacted and said, "I'm not a daughter any longer, and that woman isn't a mother anymore."

"That's beyond heavy. Shar, walk me through the rest of it."

She went on to tell me about being a tomboy to a single father and how she adored spending time with him. She thought about the call each time she showed up to work. She anticipated another call like it every time she clocked in. It seemed like there was no place to put the trauma and that Shar was going to leave her job.

I spent quite a bit of time, a few sessions, encouraging Shar to express her pain, loss, flashbacks, exhaustion, and fear. We also talked about the people who were still in her life. We talked about traditions and what was meaningful.

Shar had two school-aged kids herself, and she was in a strained marriage, but committed to finding a way forward. While she was a grieving daughter, Shar was also a loving mother and dedicated partner.

How can so much pain and love exist at the same time?

She trusted me enough to guide her through her pain. After several weeks of therapy, I began focusing on her current lifestyle. She had two kids and a partner who wanted to make things work. I planned on transitioning the grief for her father into intentionality and meaning. Her family and future could surely benefit from that energy.

"Shar, I want you to see your pain a little bit differently. You miss your father in ways that are hard to describe. You ache from the loss. This pain exists because you miss him. You miss him because you love him. Your grief and pain have been the only ways that you could still love him."

She understood that grief and love are two sides of the same coin when she said, "I don't get to love him anymore. I only get to miss him."

I yielded. "I won't fight you on that one. You have opportunities to use your love for your father with other people in your life. Anyone come to mind?"

"My babies, my friends, and I still love my husband very much."

I let the moment sink in and then I offered, "Shar, you left yourself off the list. I am sure your father wanted you to have a sense of being loved too."

The rest of our work focused on love being more potent than her loss. She missed her dad, because she loved her dad. She was able to channel her energy into her personal health and it positively impacted her family. Shar found meaning in taking care of herself so she could become a better mother and wife.

In time, she was able to reconnect with her work in the ways she used to, and her perspective was sharper. She was honored to be a dispatcher, and she knew how important her work was. She went on to become a supervisor for her agency while she enrolled in a college program. The first First Responder has her sights set on becoming a nurse practitioner.

Lessons learned:
- Recognition and acceptance of pain can lead to the creation of non-pain.
- Grief hurts because we care about the person we lost. Loss and love are the same things.
- The death of a loved one can enhance existing relationships.

The Last Responder:
Medical Examiner/Coroner/Chaplain/Law Enforcement/Fire Personnel/EMS

Last Responders have many responsibilities, and oftentimes, they include the discovery, investigation, notification, and examination of the deceased. They are also messengers and counselors of loss to loved ones and kin. They specialize in how to have empathy and objectivity when providing death notifications. That's a pretty rough gig.

Several professions step up to the responsibilities of a last responder. The cast of professionals who deal with death are police officers, fire crews, EMS, chaplains, hospital workers, and medical examiners. This conversation is with a stoic woman who worked in the Medical Examiner's office. She is a true professional who has lost much of her personal identity.

Heather called me during the late Fall. "I feel like an executioner. I have told hundreds of people that their loved ones have died. I watch hearts break on a daily basis."

We met at my office, and I offered her a cup of tea. As she was sipping it, she described her exhaustion and how she was "so hurtful to others." She was under the impression that she was the cause of pain rather than the professional who was tasked with delivering ill-fated news.

"Heather, how's your tea?" I was testing her ability to recognize anything outside of her anguish and preoccupation with work.

"I hadn't noticed. The warm cup feels nice in my hands though." She was on the verge of crying.

Sensing that Heather had a habit of putting her sadness aside so she could serve people well, I wanted to create a space for her to uncork the truths of her career. "You're wearing grief and sorrow like a heavy coat. What have you been going through?"

She was resistant to let her emotions flow. "There are two sides to my work and they both involve talking to people about death and causality. There isn't room for me to be upset with things."

"There's no room to feel. I hear that often from folks who are in similar lines of work: Cops, firefighters, EMS, hospital, military. Getting the job done means checking your feelings at the door."

She nodded affirmatively, "Pretty much."

"Heather, you said that you are an executioner of sorts. You deliver incredibly hard news to people. When you stop working, what do you find yourself doing?"

"I go home and hide." She looked at me with raised eyebrows and continued, "I eat a ton of crappy food and watch bad TV."

If I felt like a murderer of love, I think that I would fold myself into bed and hide too. Hibernating and shutting down are classic reactions to being burnt out and traumatized. It's the freeze response to trauma. Heather's career will be short-lived if she can't find ways to balance out her pain.

"What are your go-to crappy foods?"

"Cheetos usually do the trick. I also find that wine helps me wind down. I don't take care of myself very well these days."

I let her last comment hang in the air for a moment before I said, "Heather, I imagine that your body has been telling you to dial back and that you haven't been listening. You've probably earned some couch time where you can indulge in simple pleasures. How do you recharge so you can be who you need to be for your job?"

"I just make it happen. Show up, put on a good face, and serve the public the best way possible."

I'm pretty sure that she's lost sight of what was the best way. "You say 'serve the best way possible.' I want to take some time and get back to the basics of what that means to you. What skills and choices have gotten you this far in your life?"

"Well, I don't shy away from any task in front of me, and I pride myself on being reliable."

"I admire you for that, Heather. Consider the possibility that you have been reliable to the needs of those around you and have ignored the needs of yourself."

She perked up a bit and said, "I sacrifice myself for others. I always have."

This is the song of the servant. Give until you don't have anything else to give. Imagine if she could treat herself with a fraction of the energy that she offers her career. Sarcastically, I thinly smiled and stated, "You must not have ever heard a flight attendant tell the passengers to put their oxygen masks on prior to helping others."

Heather understood the comment and quietly replied, "I've forgotten how. There is so much required of me, and it never lets up."

"Of course, your work will never let up. There will always be another death to tend to. What happens if you can't get all your work done?"

"It will be waiting for me tomorrow or someone else will need to handle it."

I repeated the substance of her comment. "It will be waiting for you tomorrow or someone else will handle it." She let down a bit and she was considering that she couldn't do it all. Maybe she didn't have to. There could be more energy and balance for herself.

We allowed space for her exhaustion and then we nailed down examples of her identity outside of being a Warrior Servant. Her strongest skills were honor and consistency, so we dialed up a plan where she could be more in line with her principles. The more she can stay true to her own values, the greater her improvements will be. This meant reconnecting with friends and family in the area. Heather also planned a trip to the mid-west to see her parents in the Fall. She committed to getting new hiking boots and getting up in the hills, and she also made some new fitness goals.

Heather was able to recreate herself with more meaning because she was vulnerable and open to exploring pain. It is no coincidence that when she spent more time with people she loved, and engaged in the things that brought her comfort, Heather's career became more rewarding. Each moment was precious, and she became excited about her personal and professional future.

Lessons learned:

- Recognize your stress level and symptoms of burnout.
- Connect with people you care about outside of work.
- Engage in activities that have meaning and purpose.

Protect and Serve: Law Enforcement Officer

Police work is such an honorable profession. It is heroic, kind, dutiful, and compassionate. It's also shocking, humbling, and traumatic. A career as a cop can take a massive toll on personal and relational health. Law enforcement officers easily fall into the traps of an over-identified Warrior Servant. The following conversation was with an officer in a medium-sized department. He had a call that hit too close to home.

Jay recalled a battered and terrified woman saying the phrase, "Thank God, you're here!" The DV call floods his mind most days whether he is on shift or not. That particular call, where a woman resembling his wife barely survived the terror of her abuser, was impossible to shake. His marriage had taken a hit because Jay was emotionally shut down, and his inability to process the call stole any chance of harmony at home.

He had become hypervigilant about the dangers of every call, and he was preoccupied with the notion that there are bad people who hurt others out there. He thinks they're everywhere. They are lurking behind doors and in the shadows. They are sitting in the car at each traffic stop.

The traumatic call was a tipping point for a career that had seen countless shifts and episodes of pain, suffering, drama, and trauma. I asked Jay to walk the call out and describe what he was thinking. He cautiously said, "Doc, I can't tell you what I really think. Assuming you could handle it, you would make sure that I lost my badge."

"Jay, you'll know soon enough if I can hack it, and confidentiality is sacred to any therapist. I'll never be in the position to take your gun."

The next 10 seconds felt like an hour, and then he broke the silence. "That woman was beaten so badly, and the Jackwad who did that to her was nowhere to be found. I wanted to hunt him down and bury him in the desert." Jay's face was red and the veins in his neck were working hard. He had so much rage and it didn't have an outlet.

"I want to know what you are holding on to. What did this call wake up that the others haven't?"

He was still sizing me up and offered, "There are so many people out there who get hurt for no reason. So many things make no sense at all."

I reflected back and wanted to go deeper. "Jay, so much loss and pain seem senseless. That DV call hit you differently."

He didn't hesitate. "She was pummeled by some asshole."

"I wouldn't put that pain and disbelief on anybody in your position, but I imagine that you have run quite a few domestics in your career. This one kicked you harder."

"The victim looked so much like my wife. I can't stop picturing the scene when I see my wife."

Now we were in it. "That makes more sense to me now. I know it takes a special person to marry into cop life, so I bet that you can't stop imagining your wife being hurt."

He was stoic and made eye contact with me while he nodded affirmatively. After another long moment, he said, "She is everything to me. She has put up with me and all my shit; I can't stand to think of my life without her. That call opened up some things that I didn't know were there. Now I imagine losing my loved ones all the time."

"Tell me more about your loved ones and what makes them so special to you."

Jay overflowed with pride and appreciation for his wife, two pre-teens, siblings, and parents. After he described them all in great detail, he proceeded to tell me about his close network of friends from high school. He still plays in a flag football league with them, and they get their families together often.

I leaned on his love and loyalty. "That horrible DV call clarified how special your wife, family, and friends are to you. It speaks to how much it would destroy you to lose any of them."

He replied, "I can't imagine living without them. Especially my wife and kids."

Jay was a seasoned cop who was stuck in a collection of pains that stemmed from so many years in the field. Truthfully, his loved ones were healthy and safe. He was imagining the devastation and anguish if they were to be hurt or lost. He was applying his work to his home life. I countered by saying, "Actually, I think that you can imagine living without them. It is the worst pain you can think of. You see so many people suffering, and when you imagine your special people going through similar experiences, it crushes you. The thing is, you still have them in your life. You still get to hold them, love them, appreciate them."

He perked up and waited for me to offer some advice; not my role. Jay already knew what to do, and I was there to unfold it.

"Let's keep this simple, Jay. You witness bad shit on a regular basis. How can you use those awful events to improve your marriage? How can you be a better dad because of your work? What could you do with your buddies to make your hard work worth the effort?"

Laughing a bit, he said, "I deal with dirtbags all the time. It reminds me to not be a dirtbag."

"That's a solid approach. Grow that idea a bit and describe what not being a dirtbag is like for you."

He shifted into a new gear where you could see his imagination expanding. "I'm pretty good at being spontaneous with my wife. I can still make her laugh and smile. It's been a while since we got away and did something special."

"What would be special? Think of something worthy of a photograph framed up on the wall."

Almost instantly, he offered, "Mammoth ski resort. She and I have rented a condo by the slopes a couple of times before. I'm pretty sure that's the place where our kids have been conceived. She would love to go back." Jay was smiling.

"Jay, I bet that you can imagine the look on her face. What would it be like for you to make this trip happen?"

He was laughing while he leaned back in his seat. "I don't want to have any more kids, but we are way overdue for a trip together. The trip will give us a chance to relax and reconnect."

Jay spoke as if the trip was already booked. His mindset moved through the traumatic calls and into the safety and predictability of his marriage. We spent the next few minutes outlining how he could connect with his kids individually and as a family unit. He recommitted to helping out with their sports teams in his free time. He and his buddies added a poker game to the calendar once a month. This dude dialed in the important relationships and the benefits of those deep connections offered strong competition to the tough calls at work.

The burnt out cop became motivated to love on those who mattered to him; and ironically, each difficult incident helped him focus on the beauty and love in his life. His home life improved and helped him be more patient with work. Greater patience and tolerance at work helped him be more grateful at home. The new cycle of gratitude and service became a new normal.

Lessons learned:

- Our work reminds us of our personal life. Let it.
- Non-pain (love) and pain coexist. Choose one.
- Transition our stress into greater connectedness with people we love.

Too Many Deployments: Military Service

Military service is a different animal. It is more than a lifestyle; it is life. When a person enlists, they are walking away from many of life's comforts and freedoms. Any sense of a personal life is forced to take a backseat to Uncle Sam. How does one cope with the sacrifices of military service? They find connections and fulfillment within the ranks. Many of the bonds are stronger than kin. This story reveals the invisible wounds that a soldier had when transitioning into civilian life.

"Doc, you ever been to Fort Campbell in the middle of August?" Mitch was talking about his time with the 101st Airborne Division in the United States Army.

"Can't say I have, Mitch. Kentucky isn't on my list of places to go in the summertime."

"Well, it's lovely compared to Afghanistan any time of the year. That place is one big sweat stain."

"I imagine you have quite an array of memories from your time in service. What stands out?"

"I have been deployed three times in two countries. That's too many deployments. The first one was pretty damn exciting. It was fun, until a couple of my boys got hurt. Nine months flew by. The second tour was filled with chaos and loss. There were some close calls, firefights and rocket attacks. Our heads were on swivels 24/7. Third tour seemed like a lifetime, and I still haven't settled in since I got out."

"Mitch, I want to support you and create a space for you to offload whatever you think you need to. You mentioned, 'settled in.' What do you mean by that?"

The soldier, turned firefighter and paramedic, held back for a long moment and repositioned himself in his seat before he began. "The Taliban does unimaginable shit. Women, kids, and anyone who doesn't have their heads down with obedience pays with their life. A few people I served with have died, or been wounded, and I can think of thousands of civilians that have been senselessly killed, because of their desire to have a better life." His demeanor was firm, and he was well-practiced at keeping his emotions in check.

I backtracked, "Mitch, you still haven't settled in? To what?"

"Now that I'm home, I go about my days in a community that has never known war. Nobody here is afraid to speak freely. You can wear whatever you want, say whatever you want, and do whatever you want to do. This is fantasy land compared to life in the Middle East."

I treaded lightly and said, "You've seen very different worlds."

Mitch snapped back, "Understatement of the year, Doc. Nobody stateside understands the crazy shit that happens outside of their naïve, little bubble. I can't talk to anyone about what I've seen and been a part of. They would look at me like I was making things up or they would think I was a monster. Only those who have been there understand."

"I'd like to understand, Mitch. I imagine you have changed quite a bit because of your experiences. When you say that you can't talk to anyone about your deployments, does that include your family?"

Wide-eyed, he replied, "Especially my family."

I waited for him to explain.

"I've been with my wife since before the Army and she knows that I have done some really cool shit and some really ugly shit. I won't tell her the details of the ugly shit. Our two kids will never know the extent of my experiences."

"So, you want to spare them from knowing what you know."

"Doc, I've seen things that the movies will never be able to get right. I can't have my wife and girls picturing me being a part of that world."

I wanted to support his position and find ways for him to reintegrate into his life at home. I hoped for Mitch to have more peace. Connectedness was the key. "I hear you, Mitch. It makes sense that you hold back telling them about your experiences."

"Not many people understand. I don't think that you would get it either." He deserves to be apprehensive talking with me. I'm an outsider.

"I've worked with quite a few people who are trained to do difficult things, and they don't want to relive their moments more than they already do. I bet you not only want to avoid rehashing the memories, but you also don't want those sights and sounds in the heads of your loved ones."

"Yep." Mitch was somber.

"When you told me that you haven't settled in with life outside of the Army, you might have been making it harder than it needs to be."

This irritated him. "What the hell does that mean?"

"What I mean, Mitch, is that you probably want your close family to understand some things about your time in service, while not truly knowing about your time in service. Do you hear the difference between understanding and knowing?"

"I do. My brothers from the 101st understand and know what it was like. I don't want my daughters and wife to know what I know. I'm not sure I want to try and help them understand. It's easier to keep it to myself."

"Sorry, man. If it was easier, you and I wouldn't be here. Keeping your experiences and your life to yourself is making it harder than it needs to be."

Now we were on the same page. Mitch clicked in with the last comment. "Okay, so how do I talk with them? How do I connect with them?"

"I like your words, Mitch. Connect with them. You are home now, and while you brought home a luggage set of memories, you get to engage with your wife and kids in new ways. You can create bridges of new experiences with each one of them. You will find that they can connect with you too."

This resonated and the silence in the room was heavy. Mitch's wheels were turning, and he asked, "Where do I even start?"

"Go with what you know. Your wife and daughters are probably really good at certain things. I bet that they are proud of their accomplishments too.

Perhaps they could teach you a few new skills or activities. What comes to mind?"

The combat veteran untapped many stories about his wife and kids. He beamed with happiness as he described their achievements and ambitions.

"That's your compass heading, Mitch. I want you to create some new experiences with them. Connect on their terms and join what is going well with each one of them. Imagine asking your daughters to share their schoolwork with you. Notice your wife's talents and spirit. Start with what is already there and expand upon it."

Mitch was open to the concepts of joining and serving his family. "I can do that. Do I ever need to tell them about my time in the Army or should I try to move on?"

"Forgetting about a significant chapter of your life is not in the cards. I wouldn't ask you to forget about anything. I want you to bring the awful shit with you and make some meaning out of it. Where can you apply your experiences of war with your family and work at home?"

"I can recognize that my home is not Iraq, Afghanistan, or .... Kentucky." He was smiling when he said Kentucky. He continued, "My wife is the most loving person in the world and our girls are so perfect. We have a great house, and my work is pretty damn rewarding. I have a new brotherhood and I get to be in the town I grew up in."

"That sure sounds like settling in, Mitch. With time, as you strengthen the bonds that you have at home, I envision new moments where you will all learn more about each other. This includes your family understanding a bit about your past. Perhaps they deserve to see and appreciate you too."

Mitch had so many traits of the typical Warrior Servant. He grew up living and feeling the experiences that most of us do until he chose a life of service. He adopted the strength and dedication of a soldier, while burying the perceived weaknesses of pain, fear, grief, and trauma. This led to relationship troubles back home. He changed.

Mitch, like all Warrior Servants, gets to keep changing and have a renewed focus on what is important in life. Connectedness with loved ones is at the top of the list. Connect with them in authentic ways and they will get to know you at the same time.

Lessons learned:
- Recognize the differences between warrior and self.
- Your loved ones deserve to <u>know</u> you better.
- Connect with others and allow them to connect with you.

The Lonely Servant: Wildland Fire

Many Warrior Servants will have some sort of an identity crisis in their lives. Typically, this happens when major events smack them upside the head with reality. This could be sudden changes in health and ability, the end of a relationship, retirement, etc. These are moments when a person questions how meaningful life is.

Wildland firefighters are particularly vulnerable to the identity crisis because their work is rewarding, but it is typically seasonal. Who are they when they aren't wearing Nomex and a pair of White's? The following conversation with Alan offers a better understanding of an over identified professional.

Alan and I met in early February. When I asked him to tell me about himself, he said, "I'm a wildland firefighter with the BLM in central Nevada." His initial response was about his career. That was my first clue that his identity was strongly attached to his work.

"Nice. How long have you been with BLM?"

Alan was quick to tell me about his seven years in federal fire. "I cut line for a couple of seasons, moved to an engine, and I was with a Helitack crew the last two seasons."

I've spent quite a bit of time in wildland culture, and I dig these folks immensely. They are in a class of their own and the title of "Forestry Technician" doesn't remotely describe what they do. I didn't know much about Alan, but his seven years had undoubtedly held many adventures.

"I bet you could tell me some amazing stories. How do you like being on a Helitack crew?"

He smiled in a way that communicated he was part of something special. "I love it. My job is fun, the crew is full of some crazy-ass people, and it never gets old. Lots of shenanigans."

I wanted to hear about the adrenaline and cool things that he was a part of, but that was not why Alan was on my couch. "I bet your work is pretty rewarding. What's your life like during the off-season?"

He pulled out a photo of his crew this past summer. He was in the middle of eight people and was sporting a fierce beard. His yellow (shirt) was fantastically dirty. The grime was a sign of experience and respect. Alan had an ear-to-ear grin in the photo.

I waited for him to connect the dots between being the happy dude in wildland fire and sitting in my therapy office.

Quietly he said, "This is all I have. I don't have shit in my life except for this crew."

A few moments went by before I asked, "Where are they now?"

"They all have families and lives outside of the crew. They're probably having a great off-season and having fun."

Alan's assumptions about his crew revealed what he believed was missing from his own life: family and a lifestyle outside of work. "Alan, who are you other than a wildland firefighter?"

He was staring at the floor in front of his feet. "I have no idea."

"Okay, please stay with this. Try to tell me more about who you are and what you are about."

Alan's pain started to come to the surface, and he said, "I love being on a good crew. Not all crews are solid, but I found a home with this one. I fucking hate wintertime."

If it was during fire season, Alan would be piling up overtime hours and he would have a sense that he was productive. Like many people in fire, Alan's life was predictable during the season. He considered his life to be hollow, and downright boring, during the cold months.

"What does off-season look like for you?"

He teared up and muttered, "Lonely. I'm really lonely, man."

I offered some language that I knew Alan would recognize. "Your situational awareness is solid."

He looked at me and said, "What do you mean?"

"Situational awareness isn't only for a fire assignment. I think that it applies to everything in life. Your ability to recognize that you are lonely puts you in a position to make decisions. What kind of decisions can you make with your loneliness?"

Alan's face became flushed, and more tears welled up. "I've tried everything I can think of. I shaved my beard off and tried to clean up. I suck at dating, and I've never actually had a girlfriend. The friends I grew up with are all doing cool shit that makes a lot of money. I'm so damn isolated in the winter."

"Alan, that sounds pretty awful, man. I'm honored that I get to be a part of this with you. Let's take as much time as we need to prove that all cold fronts end up pushing through."

"Fire is my life. I don't have much outside of it."

"Alan, a few minutes ago, you said that you were lonely. How do you know what loneliness is?"

The question surprised him, and he raised his eyebrows when he replied, "I know when I'm not lonely."

"Okay. Break it down into the basics. Who, what, when, where, and why?"

Alan was about to reveal his own treatment plan for loneliness and isolation.

"I'm not lonely when I'm with the crew or my family in Colorado. I'm not lonely when I'm working.

April through September is the best time of the year and I get to travel all over the place. Did that answer the question?"

"Pretty much. Again, you have great situational awareness. You forgot one question. Why are you not lonely?"

This question took more thoughtfulness. Eventually, he said, "I'm not lonely because I'm proud and excited."

What an amazing comment! "Alan, proud, excited, and lonely don't mix very well. If you are lonely, then you are missing pride and excitement. When you are proud and excited, loneliness is nowhere to be found."

He nodded his head affirmatively which let me know that he understood the duality of pain and non-pain.

I continued, "Here's where the rubber hits the road. During fire season, your actions and emotions match. During the off-season, your actions and emotions match. Fill in the details, Alan."

He sat straight and leaned forward a bit, "I haven't been doing any of the things that I like doing this winter. I haven't called anybody or made plans to meet up. I've been holed up for weeks."

I pushed it a little further and said, "So, you have been feeling lonely and you have been doing lonely.

If you were fighting a fire and you were getting in a sketchy situation, what would you do?"

Instantly, he replied, "I'd move my ass and get to my escape route."

"Bingo. Make that work for loneliness."

"I need to move my ass and make some things happen. I guess I could start my preseason workout in February and not March. I'd like to go on a winter trip to see my family too."

"Now you're rolling. Let's outline your emotional escape route."

We met a couple of times over the next two weeks, and we reinforced his connections to fire culture and being an adventurous man. We normalized the existence of sadness that stemmed from being unfulfilled and isolated, and then we parlayed it into opportunities to spark meaningful changes. Alan went to see his family in Colorado, and he made a couple of detours to visit with guys from his crew. It is no coincidence that he also jumped back into the gym and beat the hell out of his fitness challenge.

Lessons learned:
- Situational awareness: Recognize what you are feeling.
- Presence and absence. Pain and non-pain.

- Create options for your situation/environment.

Lessons Learned: Concepts for us all.

Shar, Heather, Jay, Mitch, and Alan served with tremendous effort and dedication. They, like you, help this world be a better place. The lessons learned from their stories likely apply to us all. Below are the highlights of their stories. Read through these lessons carefully. Warrior Servants are always learning and training. Apply the lessons learned and seek improvement.

Shar's lessons learned:
- Recognition and acceptance of pain can lead to the acknowledgement of non-pain.
- Grief hurts because we care about the person we lost. Loss and love are the same things.
- The death of a loved one can enhance existing relationships.

Heather's lessons learned:
- Recognize your stress level and symptoms of burnout.
- Connect with people you care about outside of work.

- Engage in activities that have meaning and purpose.

Jay's lessons learned:
- Our work reminds us of our personal life. Let it.
- Non-pain (love) and pain coexist. Choose one.
- Transition our stress into greater connectedness with people we love.

Mitch's lessons learned:
- Recognize the differences between warrior and self.
- Your loved ones deserve to <u>know</u> you better.
- Connect with others and allow them to connect with you.

Alan's lessons learned:
- Situational awareness: Recognize what you are feeling.
- Presence and absence. Pain and non-pain.
- Create options for your situation/environment.

What five lessons apply to your life right now?

1. _____

2. _____

3. _____

4. _____

5. _____

Chapter Thirteen

YOU'VE MADE IT THIS FAR…
(Don't stop now)

Everything passes away – suffering, pain, blood, hunger, pestilence. The sword will pass away too, but the stars will still remain when the shadows of our presence and our deeds have vanished from the earth. There is no man who does not know that. Why, then, will we not turn our eyes toward the stars? Why?
-Mikhail Bulgakov, *The White Guard*

Many of you are familiar with a concept called The Hero's Journey. It has been studied by psychologists and anthropologists for many years, and you can find examples in mythology and pretty much every Disney movie. The general concept follows an outline where the main character (you) embarks on a journey (career in service), and you honorably stand up to adversity and evil. You get your ass handed to you in multiple ways, but you never stay out of the fight for long. You gather your strength and keep pushing toward your goals. There is usually a prize of love and peace waiting at the end of the adventure. The hero learns many valuable lessons throughout the journey and their efforts are all worth it in the end. This is the tale of Warrior Service.

If you have made it this far in your life, you clearly have what it takes to keep pushing toward greater fulfillment. Take a moment and ask yourself, "where am I on my journey?" Give credit where it is due; you have survived each day of your life and you are definitely not at the beginning of the hero's journey. Hopefully, you are not at your end either. I bet that you have learned quite a bit along the way, and you are a better version of yourself than when you began. Here is one last quiz:

The Warrior Servant Journey

1. How do I know if I am beginning the journey?

   _____
   _____
   _____
   _____.

2. How will I find the strength to keep going
    on this journey?

    _____

    _____

    _____

    _____.

3. Who will be my allies along the way?

    _____

    _____

    _____

    _____.

4. How do I know if I am nearing the end of
    the journey?

    _____

    _____

    _____

    _____.

5. What were the lessons of the journey?

    _____

    _____

    _____

    _____.

Concluding thoughts

You have become skilled at many things throughout your life and career, and this has resulted in an abundance of caution, stress, and trauma. If you don't have ways to acknowledge and release the pressures in your life, then you will slowly fall into a hole where you have regret and bitterness. This is avoidable, and the time spent with this book is a step in a healthier direction.

There are ten standard fire orders for wildland firefighters. Number ten applies to all of us, and it is a terrific ethos for living. "Fight fire aggressively, having provided for safety first." Read that again and apply it to ideas other than fighting fire. Imagine having a tuned-up and focused intent on living fully. Your approach to self-care and balance will determine your ability to fight aggressively and attain the life you want. Do you want love, wealth, friendships, and harmony? You can have it all, if you fight for it. Balance your identities of profession, wealth, friendship, family, love, spirit, and self.

This book was intended to push you toward your untapped potential. Up to this point in life, you have demonstrated many competencies for growth and success. I want more out of you, and I hope that you want more too! You have countless opportunities as a Warrior Servant. There aren't many rules to the game of life and your options are as limited as your imagination and energy. Take what is yours!

"This is not how I go."

In 2003, the motion picture Big Fish begins with a young boy, Edward Bloom, and his friends creeping up to the fence line of an old woman's house. She was rumored to be a witch who wore a patch over a glass eye, and if you looked into it, you would catch a glimpse of how you died. Skeptical, Edward boldly approached the door and encountered the woman. When he asked to see her eye, she lifted her patch and allowed him to see his death. The movie unfolds with many tall tales that stem from Edward's comfort in knowing, "This is not how I go."

If you knew how you would die, then all your stressors, anxieties, depressions, and worries would be needless uses of your time and energy. If you knew when you would die, then, similarly, all your time spent on distressing moments would be unproductive and distractions from beautiful opportunities.

The average human who has the blessings afforded by western civilization lives to be approximately 78 years old. Consider how many seasons of a person's life are allocated to pain and suffering. If you knew that those moments were not how it all ends, then you could focus on becoming a better version of yourself.

I don't think people waste time as much as they mindlessly spend time on activities that don't add value to their being. How much time have you spent this week being overwhelmed and preoccupied with things that are out of your control? What if you put your thoughts toward beauty, meaning, and opportunities? Ideations of living, rather than ideations of loss and despair, can be fluently expressed when you realize that the current moment is not how your life ends. All moments can be steered into new moments. Choose how you go!

References and Suggested Readings

Alessi, S., McCarty, R., Paolelli, M., Gonzalez, S., Massingale, F., Cloutier, D. (2020, June 19). Is suicide a sin? Retrieved August 28, 2020, from http://www.uscatholic.org/articles/201410/sui cide-sin-29503

American Psychiatric Association. (2022). *Diagnostic and statistical manual of mental disorders* (5th ed., text rev.). https://doi.org/10.1176/appi.books.9780 890425787

American Psychological Association. (2022). *Stress in America 2022: Concerned for the future, beset by inflation.* American Psychological Association. Retrieved December 23, 2022, from https://www.apa.org/news/press/releases /stress/2022/concerned-future-inflation

Berg, I. K. (1994). *Family-based services: A solution-focused approach.* New York: W.W. Norton.

Berg, I. K., & Dolan, Y. M. (2001). *Tales of solutions: A collection of hope-inspiring stories.* New York: Norton.

Bridge A., Greenhouse, J. B., Ruch, D., Stevens, J.,
Ackerman, J., Sheftall, A. H., Campo, J. V.
(2020). Association Between the Release of
Netflix's 13 Reasons Why and Suicide Rates in
the United States: An Interrupted Time Series
Analysis. *Journal of the American Academy of Child
& Adolescent Psychiatry, 59*(2), 236-243.
doi:10.1016/j.jaac.2019.04.020

Broderick, C. B. (1995). *Understanding family process:
Basics of family systems theory.* Newbury Park, Calif:
Sage Publications.

Burton, T. (2003). *Big Fish.* Columbia Pictures.

Campbell, Joseph. *The Hero with a Thousand Faces.* 1st
edition, Bollingen Foundation, 1949. 2nd
edition, Princeton University Press. 3rd edition,
New World Library, 2008.

Campbell, Joseph, and Henry Morton Robinson. *A
Skeleton Key to Finnegans Wake*, 1944.

Centers for Disease Control and Prevention,
"Suicide Rising Across the US: More Than a
Mental Health Concern," June 7, 2018
(https://www.cdc.gov/vitalsigns/suicide/index.
html).

Darabont, F. (1994). The Shawshank Redemption. Columbia Pictures.

Donovan. (2022). Peer support facilitates post-traumatic growth in first responders: A literature review. *Trauma, 24*(4), 277–285. https://doi.org/10.1177/14604086221079441

Edwards, R. (2022). How the body reacts to stress. Verywell Health. Retrieved December 19, 2022, from https://www.verywellhealth.com/general-adaptation-syndrome-overview-5198270

Feuer. (2021). First Responder Peer Support: An Evidence-Informed Approach. *Journal of Police and Criminal Psychology, 36*(3), 365–371. https://doi.org/10.1007/s11896-020-09420-z

Frankl, V. E., & Kushner, H. S. (2006). *Man's search for meaning*. Boston, MA: Beacon Press.

Hoffman, L. (1981). *Foundations of family therapy: A conceptual framework for systems change*. New York: Basic Books.

Hoffman, L. (1990). Constructing Realities: An Art of Lenses. *Family Process, 29*(1), 1-12. doi:10.1111/j.1545-5300.1990.00001.x

Horan, Marks, M., Ruiz, J., Bowers, C., & Cunningham, A. (2021). Here for My Peer: The Future of First Responder Mental Health. *International Journal of Environmental Research and Public Health, 18*(21), 11097–. https://doi.org/10.3390/ijerph182111097

Johnson, S. M. (2019). *Attachment theory in practice: Emotionally focused therapy (Eft) with individuals, couples, and families.* The Guilford Press.

Johnson, S. M. (2020). *Hold me tight: Seven conversations for a lifetime of Love.* Little, Brown Spark.

Johnson, S. M. (2020). *The practice of emotionally focused couple therapy: Creating connection.* Routledge, Taylor & Francis Group.

Kennedy-Hansen, H. (2020). First Responder Mental Health and Wellness: Kaiser Permanente. Kaiser Permanente. Retrieved December 19, 2022, from https://business.kaiserpermanente.org/insights/mental-health-workplace/first-responder-support

King, Stephen. 2012. The Shining. New York, NY: Random House.

Madanes, C. (1990). *Strategic family therapy*. San Francisco: Jossey-Bass.

May, R. (1969). *Existential psychology*. New York: McGraw-Hill.

May, R. (1985). *My quest for beauty*. San Francisco: Saybrook.

Miller, W. R., & Rollnick, S. (2002). *Motivational interviewing: Preparing people for change*. Guilford Press.

Minuchin, S. (1974). *Families & family therapy*. Cambridge, MA: Harvard University Press.

Murray, H. A. (2008). *Explorations in personality*. Oxford University Press.

NAMI. (n.d.). Public Safety Professionals. NAMI. Retrieved December 19, 2022, from https://www.nami.org/Your-Journey/Frontline-Professionals/Public-Safety-Professionals

Nicholas, S. W. (2014). *A phenomenological exploration of suicide and family connectedness*. University of Nevada, Reno.

Nicholas, S.W. (2021). *Living Ideation: A New Approach to Suicide Prevention and Intervention*. Embgro.

Nicholas, S.W. (2021). *Connect With Your Teen: Living Ideation*. Embgro.

Nichols, M. P., Minuchin, S., & Schwartz, R. C. (2004). *Family therapy: Concepts and methods*. Boston: Pearson.

Obuobi-Donkor, G., Oluwasina, F., Nkire, N., & Agyapong, V. I. O. (2022). A Scoping Review on the Prevalence and Determinants of Post-Traumatic Stress Disorder among Military Personnel and Firefighters: Implications for Public Policy and Practice. International journal of environmental research and public health, 19(3), 1565. https://doi.org/10.3390/ijerph19031565

RAND Corporation, "Suicide: Understanding and Prevention," webpage, undated (https://www.rand.org/healthcare/key-topics/mental-health/suicide.html).

Rogers, C. R. (1995). *Way of being*. Houghton Mifflin.

Rogers, C. R., Dorfman, E., Hobbs, N., & Gordon, T. (2015). *Client-centered therapy: Its current practice, implications, and theory*. London: Robinson.

Rogers, C. R., & Dymond, R. F. (1978). *Psychotherapy and personality change: Co-ordinated research studies in the client-centered approach*. Chicago: University of Chicago Press.

SAMHSA. (2022). *Responder Peer Support*. SAMHSA. Retrieved January 4, 2023, from https://www.samhsa.gov/dtac/disaster-responders/peer-support

Schulz, M. (2010). *Peanuts 60 years*. Partridge Green: Ravette.

Shazer, S. D. (1987). *Patterns of brief family therapy: An ecosystemic approach*. New York: Guilford Press.

Shea, C. (2011). *The practical art of suicide assessment: A guide for mental health professionals and substance abuse counselors*. New York: John Wiley & Sons.

Segal, R; Dundes, A; Raglan, L; Rank, O (1990). *In Quest of the Hero*. Princeton, N.J.: Princeton University Press.

Segal, R; Raglan, L; Rank, O (1990). "Introduction: In Quest of the Hero". *In Quest of the Hero*. Princeton, N.J.: Princeton University Press.

Shneidman, S. (1993). *Suicide as psychache: A clinical approach to self-destructive behavior*. Northvale, NJ: J. Aronson.

Shneidman, E. S. (1998). *The suicidal mind*. New York: Oxford University Press.

Silver, S. (2017, June 14). *Sanctuary trauma and the "sacred" This is also a problem in the USA*. No Warriors Left Behind. https://noonesleftbehind.wordpress.com/2017/06/14/sanctuary-trauma-and-the-sacred/

Sinclair. (1960). *Jungle*. New York: New American Library.

Stanley, B., & Brown, G. (2008). Patient Safety Plan Template. Retrieved August 28, 2020, from https://suicidepreventionlifeline.org/wp-content/uploads/2016/08/Brown_StanleySafetyPlanTemplate.pdf

White, M., & Epston, D. (2015). *Narrative means to therapeutic ends*. Auckland, N.Z.: Royal New Zealand Foundation of the Blind.

Yalom, I. D. (1980). *Existential psychotherapy*. New York: Basic Books.

Yalom, I. D. (2009). *Staring at the sun: Overcoming the terror of death*. San Francisco: Jossey-Bass, a Wiley imprint.

Acknowledgments

I want to thank you, the reader, for being part of our changing culture. Warrior Servants deserve more grace, love, and encouragement to be authentic. You are now part of that evolution.

This book would not be possible without the contributions of so many people who work on the front lines. You trusted me with your pain, hope, and love. I hope that I effectively described your experiences and that I conveyed how much you make this world a beautiful place. I am better for knowing you.

The A-Team

Andrea: You are my unwavering champion. There's simply no way that I can demonstrate how much you mean to me. I will take the rest of my life to try.

Avery and Jack: Both of you have a knack for connecting with me in such special ways. I love you indescribably, and everything that I do is inspired by you two.

Randy: Reuniting with my biggest big brother has been a blast. I love having impromptu happy hour with you in the garage and planning fishing expeditions. I love you, brother.

Baker and Holt: You knuckleheads keep me rooted in a world that lacks gravity. Our bonds are hard to come by, and I cherish you both.

Derek: Thank you for leading our community with sincerity and conviction. You are my inspiration for the mantra: Service first. The work will never be done, and we are just getting started! Let's continue moving the needle of cultural change.

Jacquelyn: Your friendship, camaraderie, and certainty have helped me in profound ways. Thank you for pushing me into saying "yes" to every project. You have benefited more people in your community than you will ever know.

My colleagues: You know who you are. Your dedication to ethics and constant improvement have fueled my work for years. Thank you for holding the line with doing what is right, in a culture that frequently cuts corners. I admire you all.

My editors: Thank you, thank you, thank you. You are the most patient people on earth.

Steve Nicholas has lived in northern Nevada for the greater part of 45 years. He is married to an amazing woman and a proud father to his daughter and son. Steve probably works more than he should, and he doesn't always practice what he preaches; however, he can sometimes be found playing outside with his friends and family.

Professionally, Steve is a licensed marriage and family therapist. His academic and professional pursuits have led to a rewarding career serving Warrior Servants. He proudly works with those in the military, structure fire, wildland fire, law enforcement, EMS, and dispatch.